FRIENDS

LITERACY ACTIVITY BOOK

Senior Authors
J. David Cooper
John J. Pikulski

Authors
Kathryn H. Au
Margarita Calderón
Jacqueline C. Comas
Marjorie Y. Lipson
J. Sabrina Mims
Susan E. Page
Sheila W. Valencia
MaryEllen Vogt

Consultants
Dolores Malcolm
Tina Saldivar
Shane Templeton

INVITATIONS TO LITERACY

Houghton Mifflin Company • Boston

Atlanta • Dallas • Geneva, Illinois • Palo Alto • Princeton

CONTENTS

CONTENTS

Theme 3 Good Friends

Punchouts

Consonant Sounds and Letters

Bb
bird	Cc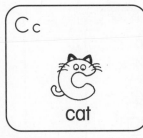
cat	Dd
dinosaur	Ff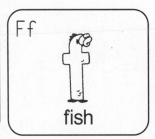
fish
Gg
ghost	Hh
horse	Jj
jack-in-the-box	Kk
king
Ll
lion	Mm
monster	Nn
nurse	Pp
pig
Qq
queen	Rr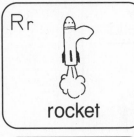
rocket	Ss
seal	Tt
tiger
Vv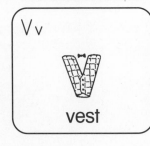
vest	Ww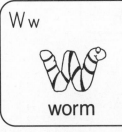
worm	Yy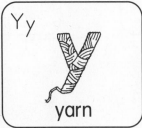
yarn	Zz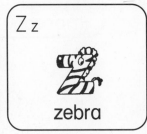
zebra

MAGIC PICTURES

Vowel Sounds and Letters

Aa

alligator

acorn

Ee

elephant

eel

Ii

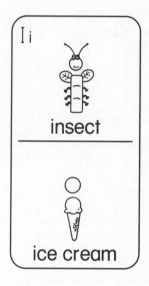

insect

ice cream

Oo

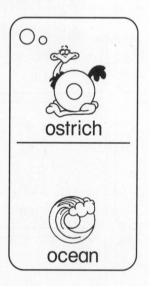

ostrich

ocean

Uu

umbrella

unicorn

Name

My Reading Strategy Guide

When I **predict/infer**, do I . . .

Look at the pictures? ☐
Think about what I know? ☐
Make a guess about what will happen? ☐

When I **think about words**, do I . . .

Try to sound out words I don't know? ☐
Try to see how the words are used in
the story? ☐

When I **self-question**, do I . . .

Ask questions to answer for myself
as I read along? ☐
Look at the pictures for clues? ☐

When I **monitor**, do I . . .

Stop and ask if I understand the story? ☐
Reread? ☐
Read ahead? ☐
Look at the pictures for clues? ☐
Ask for help? ☐

When I **evaluate**, do I . . .

See how I feel about what I read? ☐
Ask if I like what I read? ☐

When I **summarize**, do I . . .

Think about the parts of the story—the
beginning, the middle, and the end? ☐
Summarize as I read and after I read? ☐

Name

The Writing Process

Prewriting

• Choose an idea to write about.

• Plan your writing.

Drafting

• Write about your idea.

• Don't worry about mistakes.

Revising

• Read what you have written.

• Is there anything you want to add?

• Is there anything you want to change?

Proofreading

• Check your spelling.

• Check to see that your sentences are complete.

Publishing and Sharing

• Think of a good title.

• Make a clean copy of your writing.

• Find a way to share your writing with others.

Name

Let's Get Started!

What are you going to write about yourself?
Draw or write your ideas in the circles.

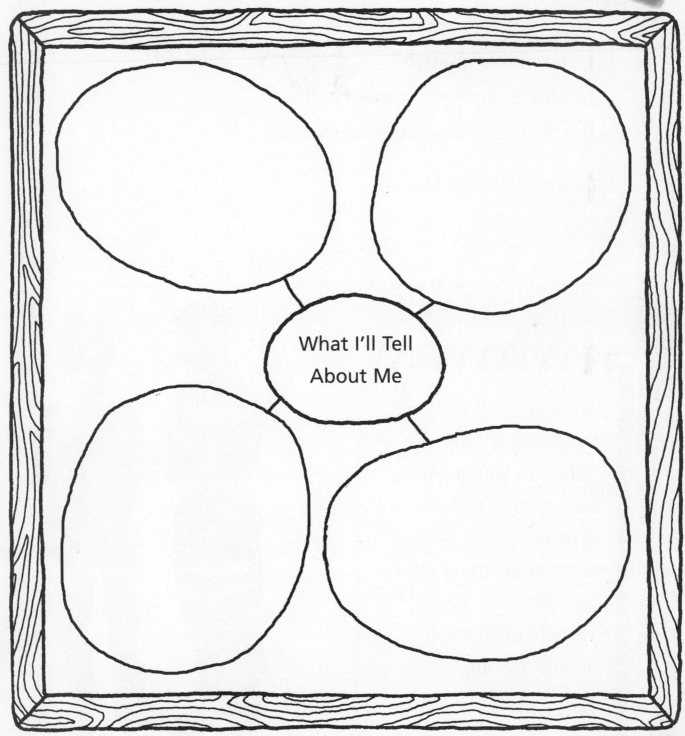

What I'll Tell
About Me

Name

Take Another Look

Answer these questions about your writing.

☐ Have I told enough?

☐ Is there anything I should add?

☐ Is there anything I should change?

Changes I Want to Make:

_____

_____

Questions to Ask
My Writing Partner

- What do you like best about what I have written?
- Is there anything I need to add?
- Is there anything I should change?

Name _Zane_   _8/9/08_

A Cat Tale

Read this story about Shadow's new
life. Then fill in the story map.

Shadow's Kittens

Shadow and her kittens lived in the quiet van.
One day a dog jumped in the van. The kittens ran
away. Shadow looked until she found them. She
took the kittens to the turkey shed. They will be safe there.

Setting	Characters
Van turkey shed	Shadow, dog, kittens,

Problem
A dog jumped in the van and scared the kittens away.

Event 1 A dog jumped in the van.

Event 2 The kittens ran away.

Event 3 Shadow found the kittens

Ending
Shadow took the kittens to the turkey shed.

Tongue Twister Cats

Finish each tongue twister. Use a word
that begins like the underlined word
and rhymes with the word at the end.

1. Cleo cleans clams with her __claws__. (jaws)

2. Stripes the stray strolls the __strery__ all day. (feet)

3. Friendly Fred __fries__ fresh fish on Fridays. (ties)

4. Snowball snatches snails for a __snack__. (back)

5. Trix gets trapped climbing a tree __trunk__. (junk)

6. Brenda brings Brian a brush and __broom__. (zoom)

7. Sleepy Sloopy slides down a slippery __slope__. (hope)

**Write your own tongue twister about a cat named
Stella. Use these words: Stella, stares, stars.**

8. _____

_____

_____

Zane   8/24/09

Name

Missing Cats

Cut out and paste the cats where they belong in the picture.

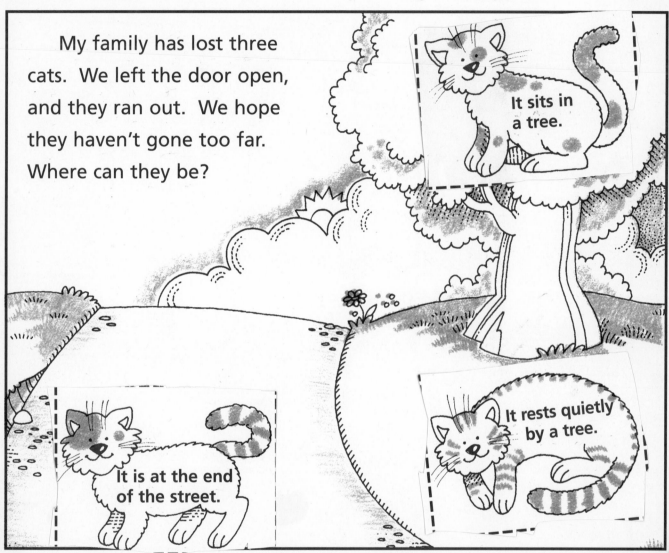

My family has lost three cats. We left the door open, and they ran out. We hope they haven't gone too far. Where can they be?

It sits in a tree.

It rests quietly by a tree.

It is at the end of the street.

Make a poster to help find a lost cat. Try to use the words **end**, **far**, **quietly**, **family**, **left**, and **street** on your poster.

Name ___Zane___   ___8/25/09___

See the Sea

Some cats are off on an adventure. Use the picture clues and the words from the box to write the missing homonym pairs.

| sail   sale | eight   ate | blew   blue | rowed   road |

1 The boat with the red ___sayle___ is for ___sale___.

2 The wind ___blew___ and the sky was ___blue___.

3 The hungry cats  ___rowed___ the boat to shore and ate dinner next to the ___road___.

4 The ___eight___ cats ___ate___ fish stew.

Draw your own pictures for this homonym pair.

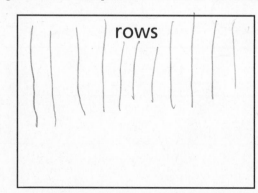

rows

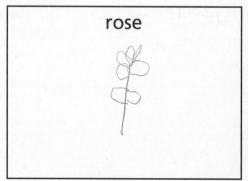

rose

Name _Zane_

_8/26/09_

Who Is the New Pet?

Use words from the box to write sentences about
the picture.

basket
children
sleeping
yarn
mouse
family
string
reading
feather
mother
father
tickle

The children are playing
with the kitten!
Their mother is reading.
Father is getting water
for the kitten.

Name: _Zane_   8/27/09

Shadow's Song

Each Spelling Word begins or ends with a **consonant cluster**. A consonant cluster is two or more consonant letters whose sounds are blended together.

consonant clusters → le**ft**, ju**st**, **ol**d

Spelling Words

1. left
2. just
3. stay
4. old
5. slip
6. drove
7. trip
8. glad

 Your Own Words

Write the missing consonant clusters on the turkey shed to finish each Spelling Word. Then write the words you made.

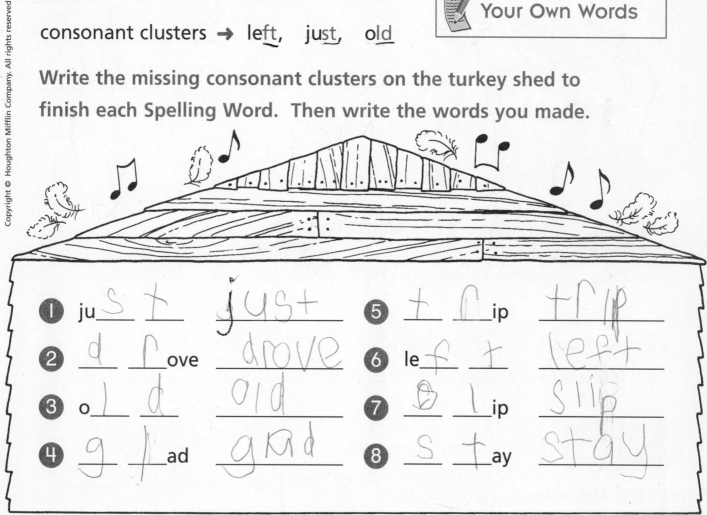

1. ju_s_t   _just_
2. _d_r_ove   _drove_
3. o_l_d   _old_
4. g_l_ad   _glad_
5. t_r_ip   _trip_
6. le_f_t   _left_
7. s_l_ip   _slip_
8. s_t_ay   _stay_

Write Spelling Words to answer the questions.

9. Which word begins with the first sound you hear in ?   _left_

10. Which word rhymes with **sad**?   _glad_

Name _Zane_   _8/28/09_

Spelling Spree

Write a Spelling Word for each clue.
Then use the letters in the boxes to write
what Shadow was.

Spelling Words

1. **left**   5. **slip**
2. **just**   6. **drove**
3. **stay**   7. **trip**
4. **old**   8. **glad**

1 to slide on ice

2 the opposite of **right**

3 a vacation

4 happy

5 to be in one place

Secret Word: _Stray_

S l i p
l e f t
t r i p
g l a d
s t a y

Find and circle three Spelling Words that are wrong in
this journal entry. Then write each word correctly.

Friday Today I found five cats. I
put the cats in my (ould) van. I (drov)
all night. There was (jist) one other
car on the road. The trip was long,
and I was glad to get home.

6 _old_
7 _drove_
8 _just_

Zane
Name

8/31/09

Under a Full Moon

Some cats got together one night. Write sentences to tell what each cat is doing.

Example: Ginger is hiding.

1. Fluffy is meowing.
2. Ginger is in the trash can.
3. Peaches is sleeping.
4. Tiger is chewing bones

Write a sentence that tells what the cats will do next.

5. _____

Name _____

I Want a Job

Read what Mrs. Piper and Jeff say.
Then fill out the form.

Jeff: I want to take care of pets.

Mrs. Piper: I could use some help in
my business. Will you fill this out?

Jeff: Well, thank you.

Name _____

1 Are you a responsible person? Write about one responsibility you

have at home or at school. _____

_____

2 What do pets need at night? _____

3 What problems should you watch for when you take care of a dog?

_____

_____

4 Which one of these animals would you like to have as a pet:

a dog, a cat, a goldfish? Tell why. _____

_____

On a separate sheet of paper, draw a poster to advertise
Piper's Pet Care Shop. Tell why it's a great place for pets.

Making It Happen

Use what you know about **Arthur's Pet Business** to complete the story frame. Look back at the story for help.

Arthur wanted _a puppy_.

His parents said he would have to show he was

responsible first.

Arthur decided to _Start a pet business_.

Mrs. Wood asked Arthur to _watch Perky_.

Just before Perky was to go home, _she was lost_.

In the end, Perky _had puppies_.

Draw a picture of what Arthur got at the end of the story.

A Tiny Ball of Fur

Look at the pictures. Read each story. Then write
answers to the questions.

Miko grinned. She held out her
arms. A tiny ball of brown fur looked
up at her. Miko smiled and said, "Am
I dreaming? Is this really happening
to me?"

She kissed the furry ball and said,
"This is the best day of my life."

How did Miko feel? _She was happy._

How do you know? _She was grinning and she_
said it was the best day of her life.

Miko was standing at her front
door. She was yelling the same name
over and over. "Max! Where are
you?" Miko's eyes filled with tears.
She didn't know what to do.

How did Miko feel? _She was sad._

How do you know? _She was crying._

Ask Arthur

Use words from the box to finish each sentence.

fish	fresh	much
splash	munch	trick

Pet Show Daily

Ask Arthur

Dear Arthur,

My ___fish___ likes to ___splash___ in the water. What should I do?

Don't worry so ___much___. That sounds like a good ___trick___.

Dear Arthur,

For her snack, my pet mouse likes to ___munch___ on cheese. Is this good for her?

Yes, it is! Just be sure it is ___fresh___.

Write a question that you would like to ask Arthur about an animal. Then write an answer Arthur might give.

Question: _____

_____

Answer: _____

The Big Sneeze

Use all the words in the bird cage to
write an ending to the story.

care
night
thank
these
watch

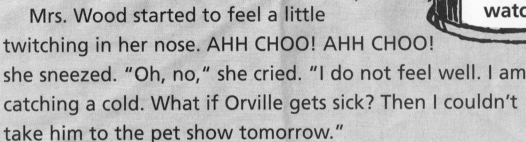

Mrs. Wood started to feel a little
twitching in her nose. AHH CHOO! AHH CHOO!
she sneezed. "Oh, no," she cried. "I do not feel well. I am
catching a cold. What if Orville gets sick? Then I couldn't
take him to the pet show tomorrow."

Just then her big green parrot, Orville, started to
squawk. "Now you've done it! Now you've done it! No
prize for Orville."

Mrs. Wood paced back and forth across the living room.
"Oh dear," she cried. "What shall I do? I don't want Orville
to catch my cold." Then she stopped walking. She rushed
to the telephone and dialed Arthur's number.

"Hello, Arthur?"

_____

_____

_____

_____

Name: _Zane_   9/9/09

ABC Fun

Help Arthur write the missing letters on the pets.
Use ABC order.

PICTURE DICTIONARY

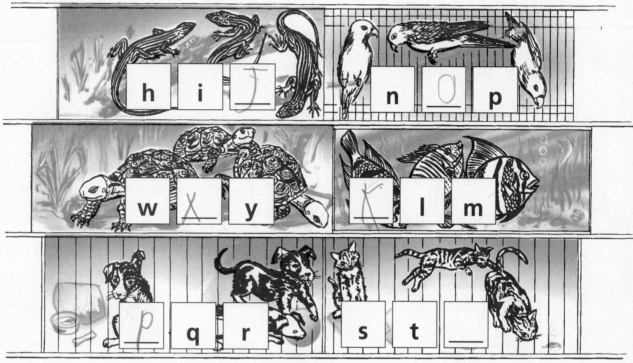

h   i   _j_   n   _o_   p

w   _x_   y   _k_   l   m

_p_   q   r   s   t   _u_

In which part of the dictionary would you find the following
animal names? Write **B**, **M**, **E** for beginning, middle, or end.

B	M	E
↓	↓	↓
A–G	H–P	Q–Z

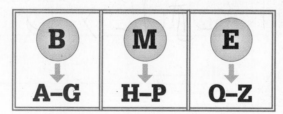

1. dog _B_
2. rabbit _B_
3. mouse _M_

4. ant _B_
5. turtle _E_
6. bird _B_

7. cat _B_
8. lizard _M_
9. skunk _E_

 Pet Show Today!   23

A Message for Sam

Write a phone message for Sam.

Use information from the picture.

I'm sorry, but Sam is not home. This is Kim. May I take a message?

Yes, please. This is Andrew. Will you ask Sam to take his dog to the park at 2:00? I want to play catch with him.

FRIDAY
6
JULY

9:05 AM

WHILE YOU WERE OUT

To Sam

Date JULY 6   **Time** 9:05 AM

Caller Andrew

Message Take your dog to the park at 2:00 to play catch.

Message taken by Kim

A Wonderful Job

Each Spelling Word begins or ends with
the first sound you hear in or 🪑 .

the sh sound ➡ she, dish

the ch sound ➡ chin, much

Write each Spelling Word on the suitcase
that has the matching **sh** or **ch** sound.

sh sound

1. dish
2. she
3. cash
4. wish

ch sound

5. much
6. chin
7. such
8. chop

Write Spelling Words to answer the questions.

9 Which word begins with
the first sound you hear in ?   much

10 Which word begins with
the first sound you hear in ?   dish

Name _____

Spelling Spree

Write a Spelling Word to finish the
second sentence in each pair.

1 The opposite of **boy** is **girl**.

The opposite of **he** is ___she___.

2 You **slice** a piece of **bread**.

You ___chop___ a piece of wood.

3 You put **milk** in a **glass**.

You put **food** on a ___dish___.

4 Your **toes** are part of your **foot**.

Your ___chin___ is part of your **face**.

Find and circle four Spelling Words that are spelled wrong
in this ad. Then write each word correctly.

 Pet Care Today

Do you wich someone could watch your pet?
Then I am the person to call. I will take sech
good care of your pet. I do not charge too mutch.
You can pay me in cass or by check. HURRY!
You get a free pet dish if you call by Friday.

5 ___Wish___

6 ___such___

7 ___much___

8 ___cash___

Name ___Zane___   9/24/09

The Animal Chorus

Find the naming part that fits each sentence.
Then write each naming part in the correct
place in the puzzle.

Geese	Dogs
Pigs	Sheep
Cats	Horses
Frogs	Cows

Across

3. ____ moo.
5. ____ honk.
6. ____ hop.
7. ____ bleat.
8. ____ meow.

Down

1. ____ gallop.
2. ____ grunt.
4. ____ bark.

Pet Show Today!   27

Name

Map It Out!

Draw or write about what happens in your story.

Beginning What happens first?

Middle What happens next?

End What happens last?

Check It Out!

• Revising Checklist •

Answer these questions about your story.

- ☐ Do I tell what my characters look like?
- ☐ Do I tell what my characters say?
- ☐ Does my story have a beginning?
- ☐ Does the middle of my story tell what happens?
- ☐ Does my story have a good ending?

Write some titles for your story. Circle the one you like best.

_____

_____

_____

_____

Questions to Ask My Writing Partner

- Does my title make you want to read more?
- What do you like best about my story?
- Can you picture my characters?
- Do I need to tell more?

A Special Pet

Laura wrote about her new pet in a journal.

Read what she wrote and finish the sentences.

teach	taught
sharing	special
learned	

Monday   In just one hour, my new pet will come home. First,

I will pick a __special__ name for him.

Tuesday   I named my pet Buddy because he is my friend.

Today I will __teach__ Buddy a trick.

Wednesday   Yesterday I __taught__ Buddy to sit

and stay. I gave him a treat for being good.

Thursday   I __leaned__ to give Buddy a bath.

Friday   I told my friends to come and play. I like

__sharing__ Buddy with them.

Playing together is better than playing alone.

What kind of pet do you think Buddy is? Draw a picture.

A Letter to Granddaddy

Help Maya write a letter to her granddaddy.
She wants to tell him all about Julius.

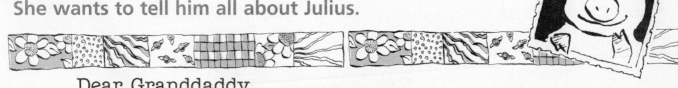

Dear Granddaddy,

Julius has been here for two months. We love to

_play dress up_____.

He loves to eat _cookies_____

_____. We go to stores and

_try on clothes_____.

There are some problems with Julius. Mom and

Dad say he is too _messy_____. He is

too noisy when he _plays records_____

_____. That is why I am trying

to teach him _manners_____. Then Mom

and Dad will love him as much as I do!

Love,

Maya

Pet Show Today! **31**

Julius

COMPREHENSION Fantasy
and Realism

Can a Pig Do That?

Use green to color the things a real pig can do. Use
red to color the things that only a fantasy pig can do.

1. take naps
2. get a job
3. tell a joke
4. win a singing contest
5. live in a barn
6. eat corn
7. drive a truck
8. roll in mud

Finish these sentences about pigs.

A real pig can _____

_____

A fantasy pig can _____

_____

Name Zane   9/29/09

A Pig for a Pet?

Write a word from the box to finish each sentence.
Cut out each sentence and paste it to the pig with
the same beginning sound as the word you wrote.

think

where

why

that

Read with a partner what the pigs say.

1. Do you __think__ a pig would make a good pet?

2. It could stay in __that__ old shed.

3. __Where__ would the pig live?

4. __Why__ do you like pigs so much?

 Pet Show Today! **33**

Zane

9/30/09

Name

Pet Show Rhymes

Complete the rhymes. Cut out and paste each animal's picture next to the ribbon it won.

① This pet can ___pick___ up fish.

And eat them from a dish.

② The second prize pet is sure to roar,

If he must ___stay___ for an

___hour___ or more.

③ Long ears and big feet win prize three!

A ___better___ pet you will not see.

④ Just look at this pet's bulging eyes.

They ___told___ me that he won

fourth prize.

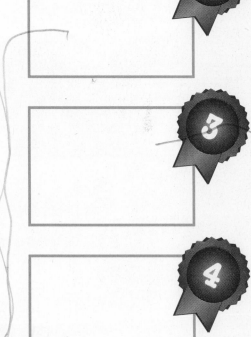

Zane
Name

10/1/09

The ABC Pet Show

Let's get the pet show in order. Read the words in
each box. Write the three words in ABC order.

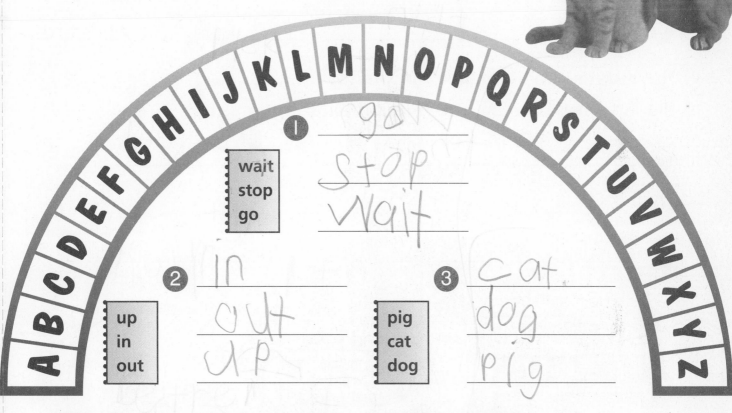

A B C D E F G H I J K L M N O P Q R S T U V W X Y Z

①
go
| wait | stop
| stop | wait
| go |

②
in
| up | out
| in | up
| out |

③
cat
| pig | dog
| cat | pig
| dog |

Write the names of three pets in ABC order. Draw a
picture of each pet.

④ _____

Pet Show Today! **37**

A Pig in the Classroom

What if Julius came to your school? Finish these sentences.

1 One day, _____ came to my school.

2 My teacher _____.

Now write three sentences that tell what Julius
did in your classroom. Then draw Julius in the picture.

3 _____

4 _____

5 _____

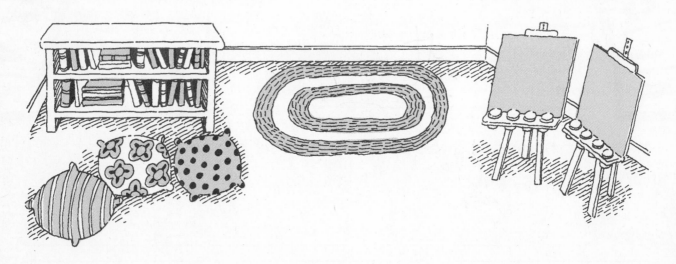

Name

Name _____ 10/5/09

Perfect Pigs

<table>
<tr><td colspan="2">Spelling Words</td></tr>
</table>

1. **that**	5. **than**
2. **them**	6. ~~white~~
3. ~~when~~	7. **thin**
4. **with**	8. **which**

Your Own Words

Each Spelling Word is spelled with **th** or **wh**. The letters **th** spell two different sounds in these words. The letters **wh** spell one sound.

the th sounds → that
→ thin

the wh sound → when

Complete each puzzle. Write the Spelling Words that have the spelling shown on the snout of each pig. Then color the squares that have the letters **th** or **wh**.

Write Spelling Words to answer the questions.

1 Which word ends with the last sound you hear in **dream**? ___them___

2 Which word rhymes with **hen**? _____

Name

Spelling Spree

Write the missing Spelling Words.

1 **thick** or <u>thin</u>

2 **black** and <u>white</u>

3 **where** or <u>when</u>

4 **this** or <u>that</u>

Find and circle four Spelling Words that are spelled wrong
in this post card. Then write each word correctly.

Dear Wendy,

   I hope you are having fun whith the
pig. He dances better thann I do. I am
glad you got the hats. Please tell me wich
one Jingles ate. I will send you a new one.
Tell your mom and dad that I love tem.

                              Love,

                              Uncle Pete

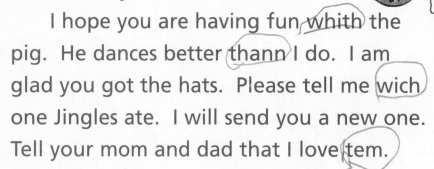

5 <u>With</u>   7 <u>Which</u>

6 <u>than</u>   8 <u>them</u>

40 Pet Show Today!

Color Me Pink

Color pink the puzzle pieces with action parts.

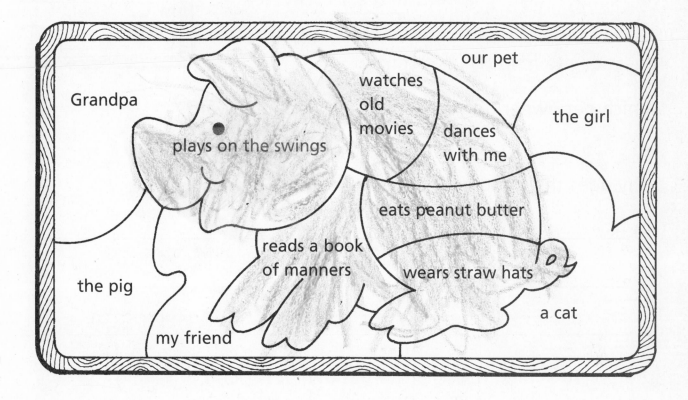

Write the action parts to finish these sentences.

Example: The pig <u>eats peanut butter.</u>

1 Our pet <u>plays on the swings.</u> _____.

2 The girl <u>dances with me.</u> _____.

3 A cat <u>reads a book of manners</u> _____.

4 Grandpa <u>watches old movies.</u> _____.

5 My friend <u>wears straw hats.</u> _____.

Name

The Award Goes To . . .

Pick a character from Pet Show Today! who has a pet. Make an award that tells why he or she is a great pet owner. Answer the questions to help you get started.

Which pet owner do you think should get an award?

_____

Why does this pet owner deserve an award?

1 _____

2 _____

3 _____

The award should tell why the pet owner is good at taking care of a pet. Present your award to the class or group. Tell whether the pet owner and the pet are realistic or fantasy.

Checklist

Before you present the award, use this checklist to check your work.

☐ My award tells about a great pet owner.

☐ My award tells why this pet owner should win.

☐ I can explain what is real or not real about the pet owner and the pet.

Name

Lights, Camera, Action!

Plan a movie about an animal in **Animal Tracks**.

Which animal will you choose?

Topic

What is one important idea about your animal?

Main Idea

What details do you want to tell about your animal?

Supporting Details

On the next page, show what your movie will look like. ➡

Be a Nature Detective **43**

**Make a story board of your movie. Draw pictures and
write sentences to tell the story.**

Tell your movie idea to a partner.

 **Be a Nature Detective**

Name: Zane   10/21/09

Name

Animal Rhymes

Read the beginnings of the rhymes. Cut out and
paste the words that complete the rhymes.

1 A turtle really can't move **fast** .

So in a race, it comes in **last** .

2 Rabbits move quite fast, I **think** .

They hop away in just a **wink** .

3 Behind the tree, I saw a **skunk** .

It tried to hide behind the **trunk** .

4 A raccoon got into our **trash** .

Before too long, we heard a **crash** .

trash

wink

trunk

last

crash

fast

skunk

think

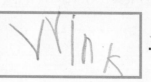

On the next page, write an animal rhyme.

Be a Nature Detective   45

Write an animal rhyme of your own.

I once had a cat,
His name was Matt.
I once had a puppy,
Her name was Fluffy.
I once had a rat,
It's name was Pat.
I once had a frog.
It's name was Dog.
I once had a hamsters,
His name was Banster.
I once had a snake,
His name was Jake.

Name _Zane_   _10/29/09_

Track Down the Right Word

The park ranger can help you enjoy a walk.
Write the words to finish her speech.

| animal | been | once |
| another | car | drink |

1 Park your _car_ and walk.

2 You have to walk if you want to see an _animal_ .

3 You might see a deer come to the stream to _drink_ .

4 A mother and baby deer _once_ came to drink.

5 Stand very still, and _another_ animal might come.

6 If you have _been_ here once, you'll want to
come back.

Use some of the words to ask the
ranger questions about the park.

_____

_____

_____

Be a Nature Detective   **47**

Zane

10/30/09

Name

What Do You Mean?

Read the two meanings for each word. Then
write a sentence for each meaning.

Example:

fly

A **fly** is a kind of insect.

To **fly** is to travel through the air.

A fly buzzed around my nose.

Birds fly from tree to tree.

bat

A **bat** is a thick stick used to hit a ball.

A **bat** is a small animal with wings and a body like a mouse.

1. The metal bats hit balls far.

2. Bats fly to the cave.

mean

To **mean** is to say the same thing as.

To be **mean** is to not be friendly or kind.

3. I'm not your friend and I mean it!

4. You're ~~I'm~~ being mean to me!

watch

To **watch** means to look at something to see what it will do.

A **watch** is a small clock you wear on your wrist.

5. I watched the butterfly drink nectar.

6. I have watch to see what time it is.

Question and Answer

Look at the picture. Then write a sentence to answer
each question. Remember to write complete sentences.

1 What is the mother bird doing?

The mother bird is feeding
the babies.

2 Which animal is swimming in the river?

The turtle is swimming in
the river.

3 What is the rabbit doing?

The rabbit is hopping into
the cave.

4 Which animal is washing its hands?

The raccoon is washing its
hands.

Now make up your own question about an animal in the picture.
Trade papers with a friend. Answer each other's questions.

Question: _____

Answer: The frog is hopping everywhere.

Be a Nature Detective **49**

ZANE   11/5/09

Name

Sound Tracks

Each Spelling Word has the short **a**, short **i**, or short **u** vowel sound. The short **a** sound may be spelled **a**. The short **i** sound may be spelled **i**. The short **u** sound may be spelled **u**.

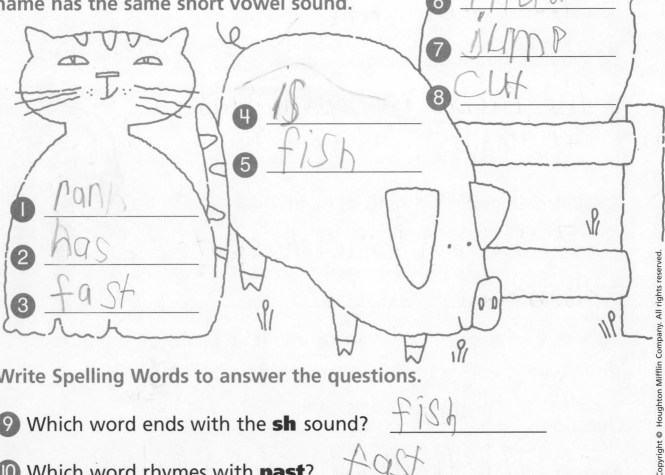

🐛 the short a sound → ran

🐜 the short i sound → is

☂ the short u sound → mud

Write each Spelling Word on the animal whose name has the same short vowel sound.

6 ___mud___
7 ___jump___
8 ___cut___

4 ___is___
5 ___fish___

1 ___ran___
2 ___has___
3 ___fast___

Write Spelling Words to answer the questions.

9 Which word ends with the **sh** sound? ___fish___

10 Which word rhymes with **past**? ___fast___

11/9/09

Name

Spelling Spree

Write a Spelling Word to finish the second sentence in each pair.

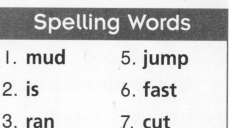

Spelling Words	
1. **mud**	5. **jump**
2. **is**	6. **fast**
3. **ran**	7. **cut**
4. **has**	8. **fish**

1. The opposite of **first** is **last**.
   The opposite of **slow** is _____.

2. You can **chop** a piece of **wood**.
   You can _____ a piece of **paper**.

3. A person has **legs**.
   A _____ has **fins**.

4. **Lions** cool off in the **shade**.
   Pigs cool off in the _____.

1. fast
2. cut
3. fish
4. mud

Find and circle four Spelling Words that are spelled wrong in this log. Write each word correctly.

My Science Log

The sun iz coming up. We see raccoon tracks in the snow. Each footprint hass four long toes. The raccoon rann along the river. We will have to move fast to catch up with it. First, we have to jemp over a stone wall.

5. is
6. hass
7. ran
8. jump

11/10/09

Name

Who's Been Here?

Unscramble the words in each
box. Write each sentence correctly.

this made who dam

① Who made
this dam?

twigs used from they trees

③ They used twigs
from trees.

made it beavers some

② Some beavers
made it.

teeth they have why do sharp

④ Why do they
have sharp teeth?

Write a telling sentence about one of the pictures.

⑤ I see its teeth,

Write a question about one of the pictures.

⑥ Why do beavers make dams?

Nature Clues

Write the words in the puzzle to fit the clues.

curious   bird
spy   eye
discover   notice
small   size
green   close

Across

1. Can you hear a _____ chirping?
7. When you wink, you close one _____.
8. When you are busy, you might not _____ something.
9. Things look different when you take a _____ look.
10. If you watch an animal quietly, you can be a nature _____!

Down

2. If you look around, you will _____ new things.
3. To know if something will fit, it helps to know its _____.
4. If you want to know about something, you are _____.
5. The color of many leaves is _____.
6. Another word for **little** is _____.

Look Closely

Complete the chart.

What Does the Nature Spy See?	
Object	**Smaller Part**
leaf	lines
branch	acorn
bird	feathers
frog	golden eye
sunflower	seeds
ice	pattern

Why does the girl's mother call her a nature spy?

She looks up close at nature.

Turtles and Frogs

Read more about two animals you saw in **Nature Spy**. Then
fill in the chart to tell how they are alike and different.

> Turtles are cold-blooded animals. They sit in the sun to
> warm up. They move to the shade or water to get cool. Most
> turtles live both on land and in water. On land they move very slowly.
> To keep safe from other animals, turtles pull their heads, feet, and tails
> into their hard shells.
>
>   Frogs are cold-blooded, too. The sun warms them up when they feel cold.
> Like turtles, most frogs live on land and in water. But frogs move
> very quickly. They use their speed to keep safe from other animals.

Turtles
Goes slow on
land.

Both
Cold-blooded

live on land and in
water

Frogs
Goes fast on
land.

Work with a partner to find out more about turtles and frogs.
Add what you learn to the chart.

Can You Imagine!

Would a nature spy ever see these silly things? Write a
word to complete each sentence so it tells about the picture.

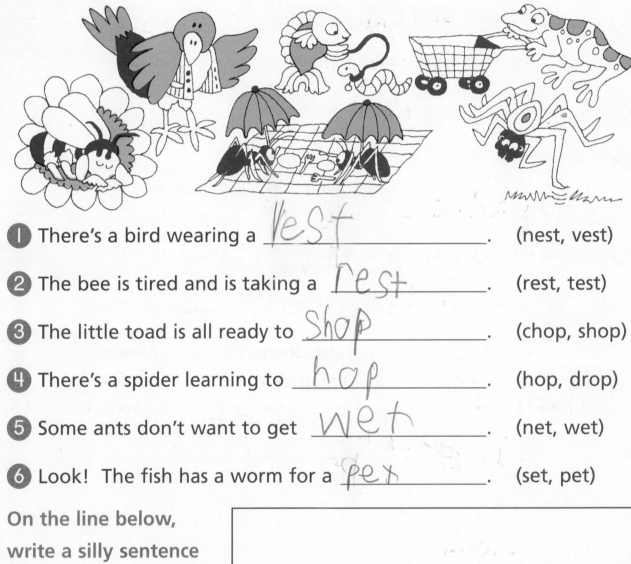

1 There's a bird wearing a _vest_____ . (nest, vest)

2 The bee is tired and is taking a _rest_____ . (rest, test)

3 The little toad is all ready to _shop_____ . (chop, shop)

4 There's a spider learning to _hop_____ . (hop, drop)

5 Some ants don't want to get _wet_____ . (net, wet)

6 Look! The fish has a worm for a _pet_____ . (set, pet)

On the line below,
write a silly sentence
of your own about an
animal. Draw a
picture of your animal.

7 _____

Name _____

Nature Notes

Pretend you're a nature spy. Write a word from the
box to complete each sentence.

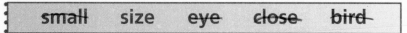

small   size   ~~eye~~   ~~close~~   ~~bird~~

I think I discovered a new animal!

1 It had the body of a mouse, but the feet of a __bird__.

2 It was __small__, so I wasn't afraid.

3 I took a __close__ look.

4 I saw it had just one bright green __eye__.

5 The large __size__ of its ears surprised me.

The animal made a funny noise. It mooed like a cow!

Draw a picture of the animal. Write its name.

monsterost

Zane

ABC Spy

There's always something to see when you're
a nature spy. Write the words in ABC order.

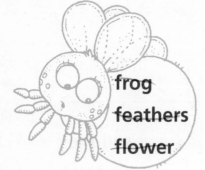

bird
bug
bark

1. bark
   bird
   bug

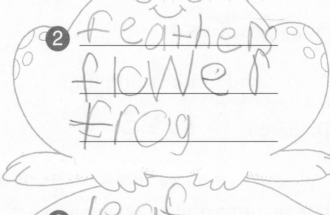

frog
feathers
flower

2. feather
   flower
   frog

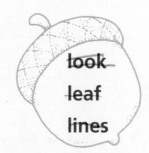

look
leaf
lines

3. leaf
   lines
   look

sunflower
seed
spider

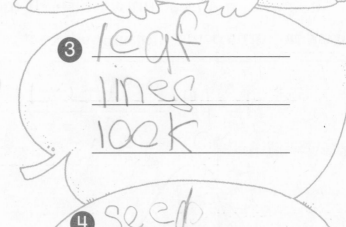

4. seed
   spider
   sunflower

Zane   12/10/09

Name

What Do You See?

Use the words in the box to write sentences about
what you see. First, write a question. Next, write
two telling sentences. Then write an exclamation.

ant
anthill
food
strong

① **Question:** What do anthills look like inside?

② **Telling Sentence:** The ant has food in his mouth.

③ **Telling Sentence:** The ant is taking food up the anthill.

④ **Exclamation:** The ant is strong!

Do your sentences all begin with a capital letter?
Do they end with the right end mark?

Zane

Name

12/11/09

Changing Colors

Each Spelling Word has the short **e** or the
short **o** vowel sound. The short **e** sound may
be spelled **e**. The short **o** sound may be
spelled **o**.

 the short e sound ➡ web

 the short o sound ➡ rock

**Write the Spelling Words on the leaves. Color yellow the leaves with
the words that have the first sound you hear in 🐘. Color orange
the leaves with the words that have the first sound you hear in 🦩.**

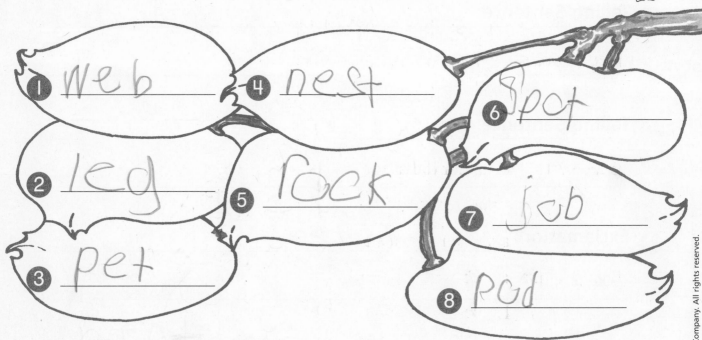

1. web
2. led
3. pet
4. nest
5. rock
6. spot
7. job
8. Pod

Write Spelling Words to answer the questions.

9. Which word rhymes with **hot**? spot

10. Which word rhymes with **beg**? leg

Spelling Spree

Write a Spelling Word for each clue.

1. It rhymes with **clock**. It begins like **race**.

2. It rhymes with **best**. It begins like **nut**.

3. It rhymes with **let**. It begins like **party**.

4. It rhymes with **rod**. It begins like **person**.

1. _rock_   3. _pet_

2. _nest_   4. _pod_

Find and circle four Spelling Words that are wrong in this book review. Then write each word correctly.

The pictures in this nature book are the best! The author did a fine jawb of showing many kinds of plants and animals. You will see a spider spinning a webb and a robin making a nest. Look closely and you can spat the lines on a leaf and the seeds in a pod. There is even a close-up picture of a frog's leag.

5. _job_

6. _Web_

7. _Spot_

8. _leg_

Name _____

Spinning Sentences

A spider has made a word web. Use words that
are joined together to write two telling sentences,
two questions, and two exclamations.

Example: They can jump so far!

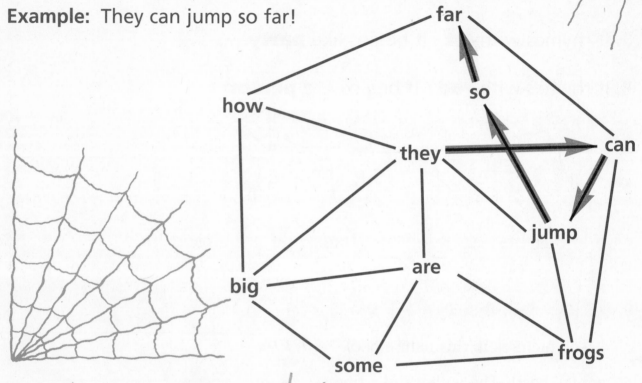

1. They are big!
2. They are frogs.
3. They can jump.
4. Can they jump?
5. How far can they jump?
6. Some are big!

Step by Step

What will your instructions tell how to do?

Write your ideas for your instructions in the chart.

Materials
What does someone need to do this?

Steps
What are the steps for your instructions? **Write them in order and number them.**

Name _____

Take Another Look

• Revising Checklist •

Use these questions to think about your writing.

Are the steps for my instructions in the right

order? _____

What time-order words did I use?

_____

What can I change or add to make my instructions better?

_____

_____

_____

_____

Questions to Ask

My Writing Partner

- Are my instructions clear?
- Are my steps in an order that makes sense?
- Do I need to add anything to my instructions?

Great News!

Write words from the box to complete this ad.

~~grow~~	open
~~smooth~~	~~outgrow~~
~~enemies~~	~~opening~~
~~goes~~	~~hollow~~

Suzy's Seashells — Biggest Sale Ever!

What does this mean?

It means most of our shells are half price.

Cone Shells Only 50¢ Each!

These shells are as _smooth_ as glass.

Chambered Nautilus $5.95!

These are cut in half so you can see they are _hollow_.

Live Hermit Crabs Only $2.95!

See the hermit crab hide from its _enemies_.

It goes into an old shell and covers the _opening_.

Feed Our Sea Turtles!

Watch them _grow_.

(When they _outgrow_ the tank,

each turtle _goes_ back to the sea.)

The store is _open_ every day.

Name

In a Shell

Think about **What Lives in a Shell?**

Then write about the animal in the photo.

snail

_____

_____

_____

turtle

_____

_____

_____

hermit crab

_____

_____

Draw and label other animals with shells.

  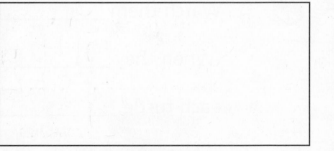

_____

Which Is It?

Is each animal pictured at the bottom of the page a
mollusk or a crustacean? Read the definitions. Then
cut out and paste each animal in the correct column.

Mollusk	Crustacean
It has a soft mushy body. It usually lives inside a hard shell.	It lives in or near the water. It has legs and a shell that fits like armor.

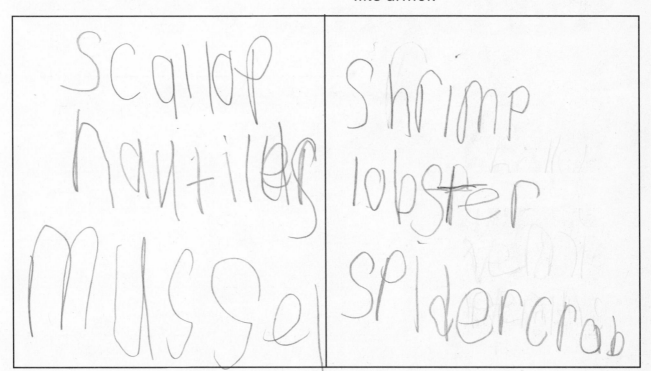

scallop
nautilus
mussel

shrimp
lobster
spidercrab

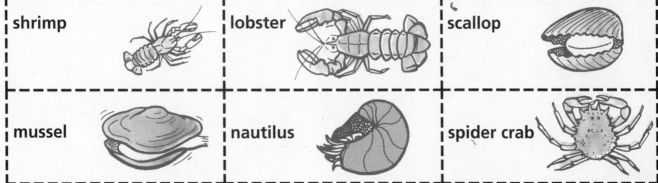

shrimp

lobster

scallop

mussel

nautilus

spider crab

Home Sweet Home

Read the sentences. Draw a circle around each word
that has a long vowel sound and the CVCe pattern.

1. A turtle's shell is its home.

2. A bear likes to sleep in a cave.

3. A snail's shell keeps it safe.

4. A nest is a nice place for a bird.

5. Clams can open and close their shells.

Now write each word you circled in the shell that has
the same vowel sound and the CVCe pattern. Add
words of your own in each shell.

wake
cave
safe
place

hide
like
nice

poke
home
close

Name _____ 1/13/10

What Lives in a Shell?
VOCABULARY
High-Frequency Words

Ex-shell-ent!

Read the recipe. Write an answer to each question.

Shellfish Stew

What you need:

4 cloves of garlic

1 tablespoon of oil

1 large can of tomatoes

juice of a lemon

4 cups of fish broth

1 pound each of scallops, clams, and shrimp

1 What goes into the stew?

garlic, oil, tomatoes, lemon, fish broth, scallops, clams, and shrimp

2 What do you open with a can opener?

tomatoes

3 Which thing can grow on a tree?

lemon

4 What kinds of shellfish does the recipe say to use?

Scallops, clams, shrimp

5 What kind of shellfish do you like most?

Shrimp

1/14/10

Name

Match the Opposites

Cut out and paste each word next to its opposite.

1 *empty* **full**

4 *sad* **happy**

2 *ugly* **pretty**

5 *boring* **interesting**

3 *back* **front**

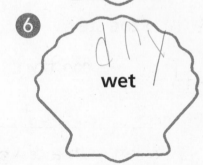
6 *dry* **wet**

On the back of this page, write two sentences using one of the word pairs. →

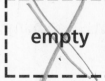 sad

 back

dry

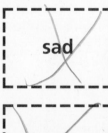 boring

 empty

 ugly

Write two sentences using one of the word pairs.

_____

_____

_____

_____

Name

What Will I Say?

Write the main idea for your paragraph in the middle
circle. Think of examples or details that tell about
your main idea. Write them in the other circles.

Main Idea

Name _____ 1/15/10

By the Seashore

Each Spelling Word has a long vowel sound.
A long vowel sound may be spelled by the
vowel-consonant-**e** pattern.

 long a → game   🍊 long o → home

🐸 long e → these   🦄 long u → use

🍦 long i → like

**Write each Spelling Word on the box that
has the matching long vowel sound.**

1 game
2 made

4 like
5 size

3 these

6 bome
7 close

8 use

Write Spelling Words to answer the questions.

9 Which word begins like **clam**? _close_

10 Which word begins with the **th** sound? _these_

1/18/10

Name

Spelling Spree

Write a Spelling Word for each clue.
Then use the letters in the boxes to find
out where a snail lives.

Spelling Words

1. home	5. close
2. game	6. like
3. made	7. size
4. use	8. these

1. how big something is   s i z e

2. this, that, _____ , those   t h e s e

3. you play this for fun   g a m e

4. to shut   c l o s e

5. the same   l i k e

Secret Word: s h e l l

Find and circle three Spelling Words that are spelled wrong
in this report. Then write each word correctly.

All About Snails

A land snail maide this shell. The shell is the

snail's home. It keeps the snail safe. It is just the

right size to hold its body.

A land snail has one big foot. It can uze its

foot to move. Most land snails have lungs, like us.

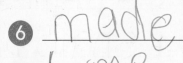

6. made

7. home

8. use

Name 1/19/10

Snail Shell

Color yellow the puzzle parts that have sentences.

Write each sentence correctly.

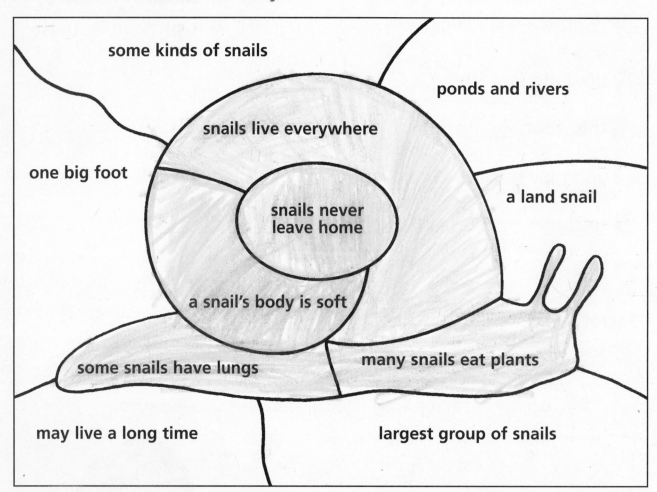

some kinds of snails

ponds and rivers

snails live everywhere

one big foot

a land snail

snails never
leave home

a snail's body is soft

some snails have lungs

many snails eat plants

may live a long time

largest group of snails

1 Snails live everywhere.

2 Snails never leave home.

3 A snail's body is soft.

4 Some snail's have lungs.

5 Many snails eat Plants

Name _____ 1/22/10 _____

Treasure Hunt

Little Treasure Island

This note can lead you to the treasure
on the island. Make each mark on the map.

1. Look for the shell at the edge of the sea. Put an **X** on it.

2. Walk past two tide-pools. Circle them.

3. Then follow footprints in the sand till you get to the
   dunes. Draw a brown flag on top of the dunes.

4. Climb down from the dunes and find the train tracks.
   Put a **T** on the tracks.

5. Look for something that has a sweet smell in one of the
   hollows in the ground. Put an **S** on it.

6. Now find something that can help you see better at twilight.
   Draw a box around it. The treasure is right underneath!

1/25/10

Name

Did That Really Happen?

Read each sentence about **Where Does the Trail Lead?**
Is it true or not true? Circle what you think.

1 The story takes place on an island in the winter. True (Not True)

_____

2 A boy walks all around and explores the island. (True) Not True

_____

3 The island is completely flat. True (Not True)

_____

4 Everything on the island is close to the edge
of the sea. True (Not True)

_____

5 There are birds, but no other animals, on the island. True (Not True)

_____

6 Some things on the island are old and not
used any more. (True) Not True

_____

7 At the end of the day, the boy is back where he
started, at the edge of the sea. (True) Not True

_____

Look at the sentences that are not true.

Rewrite each one to make it true.

Look for Clues

Someone or something is in an old shanty. Read the report.

Report by Officer Shelstein of the Beach Patrol

   I passed by a shanty by the sea. I heard a pecking noise. I
peeked in the window. I didn't see anything. I decided to go
inside. There were feathers everywhere. There were also bits of
berries and pieces of dry bread. As I walked around, I thought I
heard a flapping sound. The sound scared me. Then I smelled
something. Something fishy was going on here! Sure enough,
there were some half-eaten fish near the window. I had seen,
heard, and smelled enough. I knew what was living in the shanty.

Who or what is inside?

A bird

Write the details that helped you decide.

The flapping sound; half-eaten fish; pecking
noise; feathers

Summertime Island Message

Underline the compound words
in the post card. Then write
sentences to finish the message.
Use the words in the box to
make compound words.

boat	night	fire	sail	time	camp

Summertime Island

Hi, everybody!

How do you like my summer island?

Wherever you go on the island there is something to do.

Sometimes I race my friends across the rocks to the lighthouse.

Other times I go sailing.

I have a sailboat.

We make a campfire at nighttime.

Name _____ 2/1/10

Beach Party

Circle the words that end with the sounds you hear at the end of **band**, **wing**, or **sink**. Then draw a line to connect the words you circled. Where does the trail lead? Circle the picture.

START

bring

hook

neck

sick

hand

wig

hug

sad

wind

thank

said

chunk

book

big

swing

hang

land

pin

Use some of the words you circled to write a sentence about the beach.

_____

_____

Name _____ 2/2/10

Do You Know Me?

Write the words to answer the riddles.

1 I can be big.
I can be little.
I have water all around.
What am I?
island

4 Is it a flower? Is it a fish?
Is it popcorn? Is it pie?
My nose can tell.
What am I?
smell

2 I've been called salty
And deep blue too.
Fish swim in me.
What am I?
sea

5 Don't follow.
Don't fall behind.
Do what my name says.
What word am I?
lead

3 Eyes can be blue.
Eyes can be green.
Eyes can be the color of me.
What color am I?
brown

6 Now try making up your
own riddle.
_____
_____
_____
_____
_____

Name ___2/3/10___

Trail Guide

Read each set of guide words. Cross out the word that does not belong.

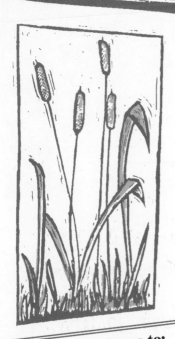

This book belongs to:

_____

pen • pot	**leg • low**	**car • cold**
pin	like	city
~~pack~~	load	~~cube~~
pine	~~late~~	cent

pan • play	**shop • soft**	**wave • wind**
~~pose~~	sleep	~~work~~
pink	small	weak
pet	~~same~~	why

fir • fox	**bat • bow**
flop	bet
~~fun~~	~~build~~
foot	~~big~~

Look up **trail** in your dictionary.

What guide words are on the page where you find **trail**?

trafficker   Transcaucasian

Write a sentence using the word **trail**.

There is a trail In my yard.

Name _____

That's Exactly Right!

Write each
sentence. Replace
the underlined
words with more
exact nouns.

Example:

Our family stayed in a <u>place</u> at the seashore.

Our family stayed in a **cabin** at the seashore.

❶ I liked to climb over <u>things</u> at the beach.

I liked to climb over rocks at the beach.

❷ There were many <u>plants</u> outside our house.

There were many roses outside our house.

❸ <u>Birds</u> woke us up by making loud noises.

Cardinals woke us up by making loud noises.

❹ We saw two <u>animals</u> along the trail.

We saw two deer along the trail.

Write one more sentence about the picture.

Remember to use exact nouns.

❺ _____

_____

  Be a Nature Detective

Sailboats in the Sea

Each Spelling Word ends with **nd**, **ng**, or **nk**.
In words that end with **nd**, you hear the
sounds of **n** and **d**. In words that end with
ng or **nk**, you may not hear the sound of **n**.

 Your Qwn Words

nd → sand
ng → thing
nk → sink

Complete each puzzle. Write each Spelling
Word on the sailboat that has the matching
spelling for the **nd**, **ng**, and **nk** sounds.

1. → s a n b
2. → h
3. → w i n d

4. → s
5. → t h i n g
    n
    g

6. → s i n k
7. → t h a n k
8. → o
    n
    k

Which two Spelling Words
rhyme with **bring**?   9 ___sing___   10 ___thing___

2/8/10

Name

Spelling Spree

Think how the words in each group are alike.
Write the missing Spelling Words.

1 clay, dirt, __sand__

2 quack, cluck, __honk__

3 clouds, rain, __wind__

4 hum, whistle, __sing__

Find and circle four Spelling Words that are wrong in this
thank-you note. Then write each word correctly.

5 __thank__

6 __sink__

7 __and__

8 __thing__

Dear Aunt Minna,

   I want to (thanc) you for letting us stay in
your house by the sea. Every evening we
watched the sun (cink) into the ocean. Then
Mom, Dad, (andd) I would take a long walk
along the beach. The sand felt cool under
our feet. But the (thig) I liked best was when
we would sing songs by the campfire.

                          Love,

                          Spencer

2/9/10

Name

Don't Get Lost!

Help the boy find his way back to his family.
He can follow only the trails that have
nouns on them.

is   from

mother   friend

into   make   train   baby   trail

sea

out   boat   the   do

up   park   rabbit

for   city   sand

boy

Now write each noun in the chart.

People	Places	Things
Mother	sea	train
friend	trail	boat
baby	park	rabbit
boy	city	sand

Be a Nature Detective   87

Making Nature Detective Pictures

Animals live all around us.

But they often hide from us.

Can you tell what animal is

hiding behind the rock?

Write two animals that live in each place.

Tell where each animal might hide.

In a Forest	Near a Pond

On another sheet of paper, draw forest and pond pictures.

Draw the animals in their hiding places. Make sure part of

each animal shows as a clue. Draw another clue for each

animal too. Write the animal names below each picture.

Checklist

Use this list to check your work.

❏ I drew pictures of a forest and a pond.

❏ Each picture has two hiding animals.

❏ I drew a showing part and another clue for each animal.

❏ I wrote the animal names below each picture.

What Is the Point?

Read this diary entry about the first day of school.
Then answer the questions.

Dear Diary,

What a day! I started second grade today.
I didn't know my classmates. And they didn't
know me! I don't know how to make friends.
Maybe the teacher has some ideas. In fact, today
he had us share things about ourselves. I didn't
know what to say, so I said that I play soccer. I'm
glad the first day of school is over. It was tough.

Author's Viewpoint
How did this writer feel about the first day of school?
He felt lonely.

Details
How do you know?
He didn't know anyone and didn't know how to make friends.

On another sheet of paper, write what the first day of school
was like for you.

Name _____ 2/22/10

Train Ride!

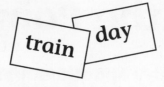

train   day

End of the Line

Train Station

Play this game with a friend.
Make six cards with **day** on them
and make six cards with **train**.

Start: Each player places a marker
on the **Train Station**. Mix
the cards.

1. Take a card.
2. Move your marker to the word with
   a long **a** sound that has the same
   spelling as the word on the card.
3. Read the word and use it in a
   sentence.
4. If you can't read the word, go back
   one space.
5. Your turn is over. The next player
   gets a turn.

The first one to get to the **End of
the Line** wins.

Train Station column:
sand
main
tray
braid
may
lap
stray

End of the Line column:
brain
play
game
pay
say
gate
grain
stay

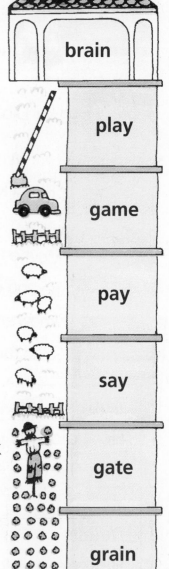

Bottom row:
paint   tame   gray   chain   map

This Way →

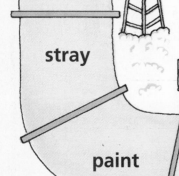

Name

A Reply to a Friend

Read this letter from one friend to another.

Dear Ricky,

How do you like your new school? Have you found many boys and <u>girls</u> to play with yet?

When you moved away <u>last</u> summer, I <u>didn't</u> have anyone to play with for a while. And you know I don't like to play by <u>myself</u>.

Did you know I am <u>flying</u> up to see you next year? Please write me <u>soon</u> and let me know how you are.

Your friend,

Terry

Write an answer. Use some of the underlined words.

Dear Terry,

_____

_____

_____

_____

_____

_____

Your friend,

Ricky

Name

Word Family Trees

Find the word families for **care**, **farm**, and **bake**, and write them on the family trees. Then make your own word family tree.

cares

farming

farmer

careful

bakery

| c | a | r | e |

c	a	r	e	l	e	s	s
c	a	r	e	f	u	l
c	a	r	e	s

| b | a | k | e |

b	a	k	e	r	y
b	a	k	e	d
b	a	k	e	r

| f | a | r | m |

f	a	r	m	i	n	g
f	a	r	m	e	d
f	a	r	m	e	d

_____

_____

_____

baker

farmed

careless

baked

_____
Name

Keep in Touch!

Write your address in the first box. Then write the
addresses of two of your friends.

My Address

Zane Kight
12262 setherscove ct.
Granger, IN 46530

My Friend's Address

Jacob Thompson
12280 setherscovect
Granger, IN 46530

My Friend's Address

Brock Trump 13
12281 Pennyroyal Ln.
Granger, IN 46530

Hooray for A!

Each Spelling Word has the long **a** vowel
sound. This vowel sound may be spelled
ay or **ai**.

the long a sound ➔ play, train

**Write each Spelling Word on the easel that has the
matching spelling for the long a sound.**

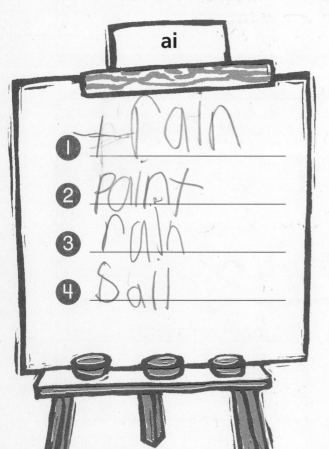

ai

1. train
2. paint
3. rain
4. sail

ay

5. play
6. bay
7. way
8. pay

Which two Spelling Words begin with consonant clusters?

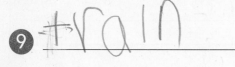
9. train

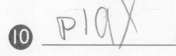
10. play

Name _____ 2/26/10

Spelling Spree

Write a Spelling Word to finish each sign.
Begin each word with a capital letter.

Spelling Words	
1. train	5. way
2. play	6. rain
3. day	7. sail
4. paint	8. pay

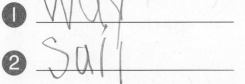

One ___(1)___

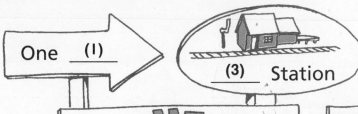

___(3)___ Station

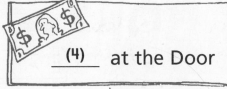

___(2)___ Today!

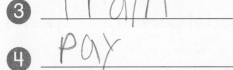

___(4)___ at the Door

① __Way__

② __Sail__

③ __Train__

④ __Pay__

Find and circle four Spelling Words that are spelled wrong
in this play. Then write each word correctly.

A New School in a New Land

Mom: This is a big daye for you, Suki. Do you want me to drive
you to school?

Suki: No, Mom, I know the way.

Mom: Take an umbrella. It is going to rayn.

Suki: I hope somebody will plai with me. When I get home,
I will paynt you a picture of my new school.

⑤ __day__

⑥ __rain__

⑦ __play__

⑧ __paint__

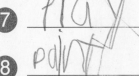

Special Friends

Write each sentence. Use the name of a
special person, place, or thing in place of
each picture clue.

special person   special place   special thing

1 I will visit my friend  .

I will visit my friend J.J.

2 Her house is on _____ .

Her hous ison Brick Road.

3 The name of her school is _____ .

The name of her school is Horizon.

4 She has a sister named _____ .

She has a sister named Liz.

5 Her cat is named _____ .

Her cat is named Max

Name _____ 3/16/10

Telephone Talk

Read what Ronald told his friend
James on the phone one night.
Write what James answered. Use
at least five words from the box.

best	frames	squint
blink	lenses	still
blue	round	
don't	sharp	

Ronald: Last week my teacher said that I may need glasses.
I do my best to read the words on the board, but the letters
aren't very sharp or clear anymore. What do you think?

James: _I saw you squint in school._

Ronald: Sometimes I squint my eyes until they're nearly
shut and blink them until my lids hurt. But that still doesn't help.
Do you ever do that?

James: _I don't have to squint._

Ronald: Today, I took the lenses out of an old pair of blue
sunglasses and tried on the frames. The round frames don't look
too bad. In fact, they look good with my round head. Ha!

James: _I think blue round frames._
are best.

Take a Good Look

Use what you know about **Watch Out, Ronald Morgan!** to complete this story map.

Characters:
miss tyler, Ronald michael, Dr. sims

Setting:
Dr. office, scool the shop

Problem:
He can't see well, and makes mistakes.

Event:
He fed the fish gerbil food

Event:
He gets glasses

Event:
He still makes mistakes. He takes off his glasses.

Ending:
miss Tyler writes him a note. He wears his glasses.

Use your story map to retell the story to a friend.

3|18|10

Name

Help!

The children in Miss Tyler's classroom are very helpful.

Cut out the four pictures of children. Paste the pictures
of helpful children in the classroom scene above. Write one
sentence that supports the generalization.

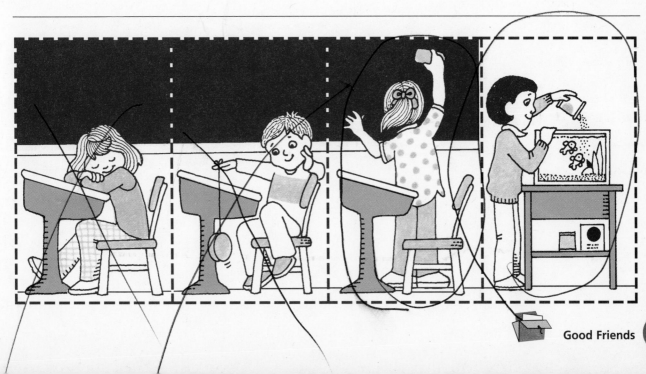

Good Friends **99**

Speak Before He Leaps!

Each pair of sentences warns Ronald about something.
Write a word with **ea** or **ee** to complete each sentence.

❶ Stop! Don't _____feed_____ that to the gerbil.

| feed | feet |

Gerbils don't _____eat_____ candy.

| read | eat |

❷ Wear a warm hat on your _____head_____.

| bread | head |

You will _____need_____ one on this cold day.

| need | heat |

❸ Hey! There's a _____leak_____ in your cup.

| squeak | leak |

You'd better _____clean_____ up that mess.

| clean | dream |

Write a pair of sentences of your own to warn
Ronald about something. Use words with **ea** or **ee**.

_____

_____

_____

_____

Good Friends **101**

Name

Let It Snow

Help Ronald Morgan make a snow person by using the words in the box to complete the directions. Then follow the directions and make a snow person.

| round |
| still |
| best |
| Don't |
| blue |

How to Make a Snow Person

1 Do your ___best___ to follow these directions.

2 Draw three circles, one on top of the other. The top one is the smallest, and the bottom one is the largest. Make the circles nice and ___round___ .

3 Draw a face on the smallest circle. ___Don't___ forget to draw a nose.

4 You ___still___ aren't done. Add a hat.

5 Draw a striped scarf around the snow person's neck. Color the stripes red and ___blue___ .

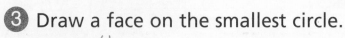

Words to Watch

Find three words in **Watch Out, Ronald Morgan!** that you do not understand. Look up each word in the dictionary and complete the dictionary entry.

Entry word: _____

Meaning: _____

_____

Entry word: _____

Meaning: _____

_____

Entry word: _____

Meaning: _____

_____

Make your own dictionary. Label a sheet of paper for each letter of the alphabet. Cut out the entries and paste them on the correct pages. Add words as you read more stories.

Name _____

Read This!

What is your favorite book? Write a
book report about it. Remember to
draw a line under the title.

The title is _____

The author is _____

This book is about _____

_____

_____

_____

_____

_____

I think this book _____

_____

_____

_____

_____

Name

Keep Your Eyes Open

Each Spelling Word has the long **e** vowel sound.
This vowel sound may be spelled **ee** or **ea**.

the long e sound ➜ see, read

Connect the words with the long **e** sound to
reach Ronald's eyeglasses. Then write each
Spelling Word on the eye chart that has the
matching spelling for the long **e** sound.

Spelling Words

1.	**see**	5.	**team**
2.	**read**	6.	**green**
3.	**need**	7.	**speak**
4.	**please**	8.	**feed**

Your Own Words

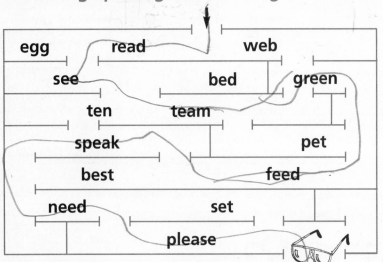

ee

1. green
2. See
3. need
4. feed

ea

5. read
6. speak
7. team
8. please

**Write Spelling Words to answer
the questions.**

9 Which word begins like **grow**?

green

10 Which word begins and ends like **rod**?

feed

3/24/10

Name

Spelling Spree

Write the word that goes with each clue.

1 talk   _speak_

2 rhymes with **tree**   _see_

3 red, yellow, ____   _green_

4 ____ and write   _read_

5 a baseball ____   _team_

Find and circle three Spelling Words
that are spelled wrong in these rules.
Write each word correctly.

School Rules

- Remember to fede the gerbil.

- Don't throw snowballs and
  pleaze don't slide on the ice.

- If you cannot read this, you
  nead glasses!

6 _feed_

7 _please_

8 _need_

3/25/10

Name _____

Time Out for Kickball

Ronald isn't sure which pronoun can take the place of
each word or words. Help him by writing the correct
pronoun on the other half of the kickball.

| he   she   it   they |

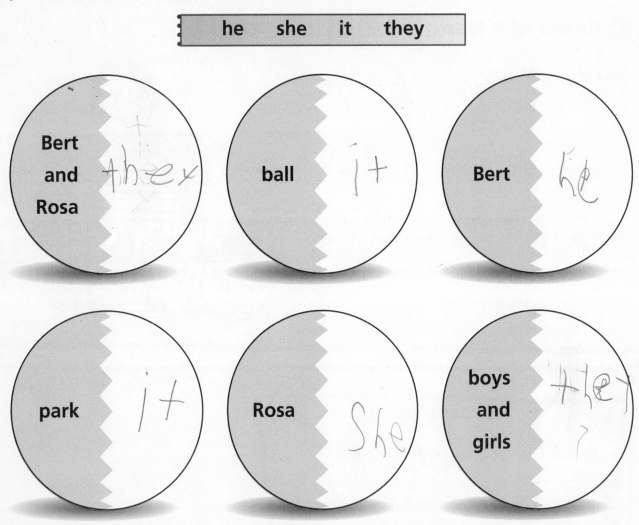

Bert and Rosa — *they*

ball — *it*

Bert — *he*

park — *it*

Rosa — *She*

boys and girls — *they?*

Finish this story. Use at least two pronouns in your sentences.

Bert and Rosa played kickball after school. *They played*
at the park. It was fun.

Name

What Am I Going to Say?

What are you going to write about? Draw or write your idea in the middle circle. Then write in the other circles some of the special things you want to tell about in your letter.

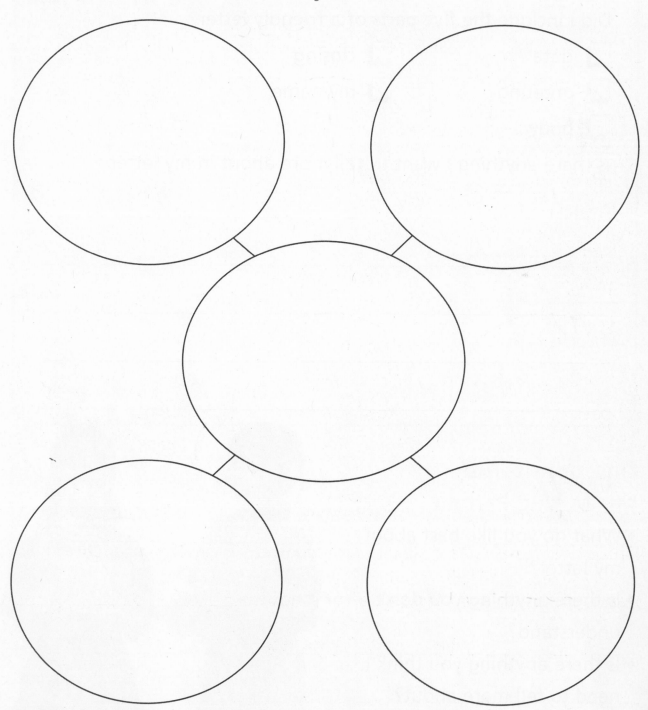

Name

Check It Out!

• Revising Checklist •

Ask yourself these questions about your writing.

Did I include the five parts of a friendly letter?

☐ date   ☐ closing

☐ greeting   ☐ my name

☐ body

Is there anything I want to tell more about in my letter?

_____

_____

_____

_____

Questions to Ask
My Writing Partner

- What do you like best about my letter?

- Is there anything you don't understand?

- Is there anything you think I need to tell more about?

3/31/10

Name

Help Wanted

Read the want ad. Write the word to complete
each sentence. Finish the sentence at the end.

| wish | sneaked | crawled | boy | while |
| angry | through | heard | miss | |

I've ___heard___ that great baby-sitters are out there.

We need one during summer vacation. My sister is one year old, and I am

an eight-year-old ___boy___.

You must be able to chase my sister. She has gotten into things ever

since she has ___crawled___. And you can't get

___angry___ when I play superheroes. The last baby-sitter

quit when I ___sneaked___ up on her and stormed

___through___ the house. We want to have fun

___while___ you are with us. Then we'll

___miss___ you when you leave. If you are a great

baby-sitter, I ___wish___ you would call me.

P.S. Some things that my sister and I would like to do this summer are

_____

_____

Name ....

Baby-sitter Advice

Finish each sentence about What Kind of Baby-sitter Is This?

1 Kevin felt angry because

_____

_____

_____

3 Kevin saw Aunt Lovey

_____

_____

_____

2 Aunt Lovey came over to baby-sit. Kevin thought she

would _____

_____

_____

4 Kevin discovered that he and

Aunt Lovey _____

_____

He decided that _____

_____

How can you use what you learned from the story to be better friends with your own baby-sitter? Write your ideas.

_____

_____

_____

_____

112 **Good Friends**

Baby-sitters for Hire

Read what the baby-sitters say. Which one would you
choose for a baby-sitter? Explain why.

My name
is Roberta. I'm a sports nut.
On rainy days, we can watch sports on
TV. When it's nice, we can play in the
park. I don't like to cook, so we
can order pizza.

My name is Ana. I like
to put on plays and go on
long nature walks. I also make
terrific fudge brownies.

_____

_____

_____

_____

_____

Name

New Tricks for Old Words

Read each sentence. Follow the directions to change the underlined word to a different word with **oa** or **ow**.
Write the new word in the box. Then use it in a sentence.

1 Aunt Lovey saw an ad for <u>soap</u> on TV.
Change the **s** to **c** and the **p** to **t** to make something to wear.

coat _____

_____

2 Kevin sat <u>down</u> with her, and they watched the ball game.
Change the **d** to **t** and you have a place where people live.

town _____

_____

3 They watched the star player <u>throw</u> a fastball to the batter.
Take away the **th** and you have what someone does in a boat.

row _____

_____

4 Kevin watched the ball <u>float</u> right past the batter.
Change the **fl** to **g** and you have an animal that lives on a farm.

goat _____

_____

Name _____ 4/6/10

What Kind of
Baby-sitter Is This?
VOCABULARY
High-Frequency Words

Mix and Match

Cut out the words at the bottom and paste them on the
matching shapes. Then write your own words to finish
the sentences.

Kevin's New Job

Today I'm taking care of a little boy. He was pretty good while I

was ___playing___ with him. But then he started

___runing___ ⬛ through the house and up and

down the stairs.

Now he's ___crxing___. I think he might ⬠ miss

___his Arents___. I ⬭ wish she'd get back. Wait!

Was that a ___car___ I ⬭ heard in the

___grage___? Hurray! She's back. Baby-sitting is

___over___!

⬡ miss   ⬭ heard   ⬡ through   ⬭ wish

4/7/10

Take a Look Around

Use guide words to find each word in your dictionary. Write
the guide words that are on the page with the word.

Word	Guide Words
baby-sitter	azure bacillus
bath	bake bawl
school	schemer science
scratch	scraping scripture
porch	Pop Port
pour	Pottage PP

For each set of guide words, write a word that you might find
on that page. Use your dictionary for ideas.

Guide Words	Word
fold • fox	
woman • worth	
place • plum	
hand • have	

....   4/8/10

Name

**What Kind of
Baby-sitter Is This?**

WRITING SKILLS   **Writing an
Invitation**

Come One, Come All!

Imagine that your class is having a party. What kind
of party will it be? Invite someone. Draw pictures
on your invitation.

To _____

Please come to _____

_____

Date _____

Time _____

Place _____

_____

Given by _____

4/8/10

Name

Go Team!

Each Spelling Word has the long **o** vowel
sound. The long **o** sound may be spelled
oa or **ow**.

the long o sound ➔ soap, own

Spelling Words

1. **own**   5. **bowl**
2. **soap**   6. **slow**
3. **coat**   7. **road**
4. **show**   8. **boat**

Your Own Words

Write the missing letters to make Spelling Words.
Then write the words under the pennants that have
the matching spelling for the long **o** sound.

sh __o__ __w__   r __o__ __a__ d   __o__ __w__ n

b __o__ __w__ l   c __o__ __a__ t   s __o__ __a__ p

sl __o__ __w__   b ___ ___ t

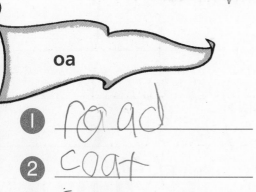

oa
1. road
2. coat
3. soap
4. boat

ow
5. show
6. slow
7. bowl
8. own

Which two Spelling Words rhyme with goat?

9. coat

10. boat

4/9/10

Name

Spelling Spree

Write the Spelling Word that answers the question and rhymes with the word in **dark print**.

Spelling Words	
1. **own**	5. **bowl**
2. **soap**	6. **slow**
3. **coat**	7. **road**
4. **show**	8. **boat**

1. What is a jacket for a bearded animal?

   a **goat** ____

2. What is a bird that does not fly fast?

   a ____ **crow**

3. What is a ship in a parade?

   a **float** ____

4. What is a program about pretty ribbons?

   a **bow** ____

1. *coat*
2. *slow*
3. *boat*
4. *show*

Find and circle four Spelling Words that are spelled wrong in these riddles. Then write each word correctly.

5. Why did the chicken cross the **roade**?

   to get to the other side

6. What kind of soup is in an artist's **bole**?

   doodle soup

7. What kind of bath can you take

   without **sowp** and water?

   a sunbath

8. What do you do if your **owen** tooth

   falls out?

   get toothpaste

5. *road*
6. *bowl*
7. *soap*
8. *own*

Name _____ 4/12/10

Words and More Words

Finish this puzzle. Write the noun from the box that goes with each picture clue. You may need to add **s** or **es**.

card 4	hat 3
~~brush~~ 5	cup 3
watch	~~cake~~ 4
box 3	~~bus~~ 3
star 4	dish 7

Across

3.

5.

8.

10.

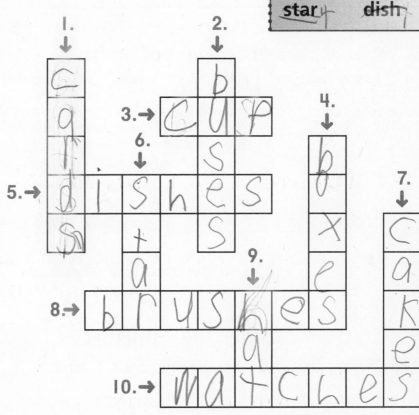

Down

1.

2.

7.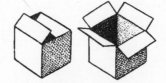

6.

9.

Name _____

Dear Diary

Use the words below to complete Monday's diary entry. Then write a diary entry for Tuesday.

write   copied   matching   both

Monday

   Today was my first day at school. My teacher wore a red dress

with _____ red shoes. Everyone thought she looked

so pretty.

   I had to _____ a story. My friend Maria and I

_____ wrote about our black cats. It was just a

coincidence. But then Maria said that if I ever _____

her again, she would not be my dear friend.

Tuesday

_____

_____

_____

_____

Name

Why Be a Copycat?

Pretend you are Ruby. Complete the lines below to make a
poster that will help a new classmate make friends.

Miss Hart will

Angela will

The best way to make new friends is

Name _____ 4/20/10

What If. . . and Then?

Pretend there is a new boy in your class. Write
possible causes and effects to complete the chart.

Cause	Effect
The new boy in your class can't find his pencil.	You loan him a pencil.
The boy forgot his lunch.	You offer to share your lunch with him.
The new boy gets lost trying to find the library.	You show him where it is,
The new boy is lonely,	You ask the new boy to come over and play after school.

Finish this story.

Johanna gave Maria a present. Maria didn't like it. She _____

took it and said "Thank you." .

Maria answered the telephone. It was Johanna. Before

Maria could say anything, Johanna said, " Come over and

play ."

Ruby the Copycat
PHONICS/DECODING Vowel
Pair: *ou*

Hopping Around

Help Ruby's friends play Word Hopscotch. Each friend has chosen an **ou** word and will hop to words with the same sound. Write **ou** words in the boxes to match **ou** sounds on the shoes.

| ~~mouse~~ | ~~could~~ | ~~announced~~ | ground |
| ~~you~~ | ~~around~~ | ~~blouse~~ | ~~should~~ |

house → mouse around
house → announced
house → blouse ground

through → you

would → could
would → should

Now write a sentence using one of the words from the boxes.

_____

Name 4/22/10

Contraction Crossword

Write the contraction for each pair of words. The apostrophes are marked in the right places.

Across

2. are not
5. we are
6. I am

Down

I. you are
3. they will
4. she is

1.
2.
3.
4.
5.
6.
you're
aren't
they'll
she's
we're
I'm

Pretend Ruby is giving Angela a hopping lesson. Write what each friend says. Use a contraction in each sentence.

Ruby says: "______________________________"

Angela answers: "______________________________"

Name _____

School Notes

black	both
~~Dear~~	ever

(box shows: ~~black~~ ~~both~~ ~~Dear~~ ever)

Use the words from the box to finish Angela's note.

Dear _____ Ruby,

Why do you have to dress just like me? I wear a red bow.

Then you wear a red bow. I wear a _black_ _____

dress, so you wear one too. We _both_ _____ don't

always have to wear the same thing. Don't you

ever _____ think about wearing something just

because you like it?

Angela

Write Ruby's answer. Use the words **pretty** and **write**.

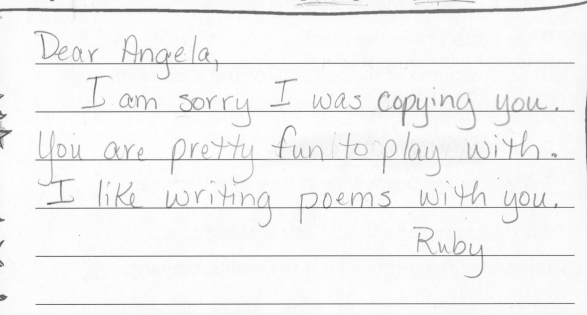

Dear Angela,
  I am sorry I was copying you.
You are pretty fun to play with.
I like writing poems with you.
                        Ruby

Name

What's Where?

Help Ruby finish the picture. Read and follow the directions.

1 Draw an apple on the desk.

2 Draw a clock by the door.

3 Draw a fish under the plant.

4 Draw a window at the left side of the classroom.

5 Draw a book on top of the bookshelf.

6 Draw a poster over the desk.

7 Tell where the boy will be if he walks backward.

He will be out the door.

8 Tell where the girl will be if she walks forward.

She will be at the desk.

128 Good Friends

Name

Exactly!

Read each noun below. Write an exact noun for it. One is done for you. Choose nouns from the box, or use your own.

> dog
> **Ms. Lincoln**
> **Land Park**
> **Mr. Hart**
> soccer
> library
> chess
> kitten

Example:

child   **Carlos**

1. game   Soccer
2. place   Land Park
3. pet   Dog
4. woman   Mom
5. friend   Jacob

Write two sentences about your friends at school.
Use two exact nouns in each one.

_____

_____

_____

_____

4/28/10

Name

It's a Shorter Word

Each Spelling Word is a contraction. A **contraction** is a short way of saying or writing two words. An apostrophe takes the place of the letter or letters that are left out.

I am ➔ I'm   we will ➔ we'll

Spelling Words

1. **I'm**   5. ~~that's~~
2. ~~don't~~   6. ~~we'll~~
3. **it's**   7. **isn't**
4. ~~didn't~~   8. ~~you're~~

 Your Own Words

Write a contraction for each pair of words on the sweaters. Then circle on the sweaters the letter or letters that the apostrophe takes the place of.

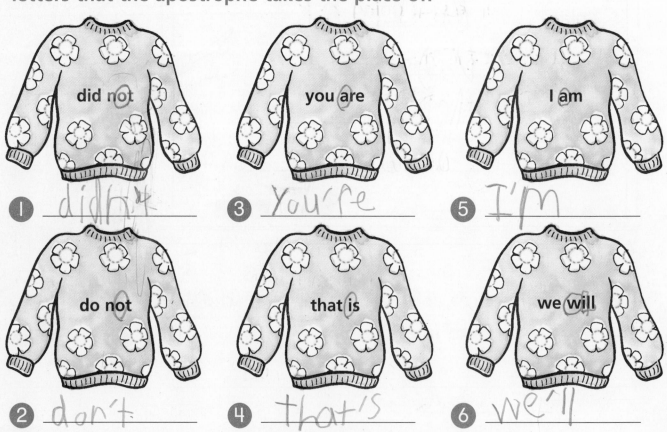

did not

you are

I am

1 ___didn't___   3 ___You're___   5 ___I'm___

do not

that is

we will

2 ___don't___   4 ___that's___   6 ___we'll___

Which two Spelling Words begin with the short i sound?

7 ___it's___   8 ___isn't___

4/29/10

Name

Spelling Spree

Spelling Words

1. I'm   5. that's
2. don't   6. we'll
3. it's   7. isn't
4. didn't   8. you're

Write a Spelling Word to finish each poem.

1. I wrote a poem about a cat.

Please, my friend, _____ copy that.

2. If you wear a dress that looks like mine,

Do you really think _____ both look fine?

3. Ruby, _____ a copycat!

Would you please stop doing that?

4. When they did the Ruby Hop,

The children _____ want to stop!

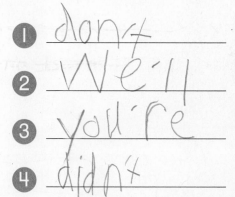

1. don't
2. we'll
3. you're
4. didn't

Find and circle four Spelling Words that are spelled wrong in these instructions. Then write each word correctly.

Rainbow T-shirts

Do you like the T-shirt I'me wearing?
You may think making one is hard, but its'
simple. Paint a rainbow on a clean shirt.
Let the shirt dry overnight, and thats all
you have to do. Now is'nt that easy?

5. I'm
6. It's
7. that's
8. isn't

Name

Search for More Than One

The nouns in the picture name one.
Circle in the puzzle nouns that name
more than one.

man   woman   child
foot

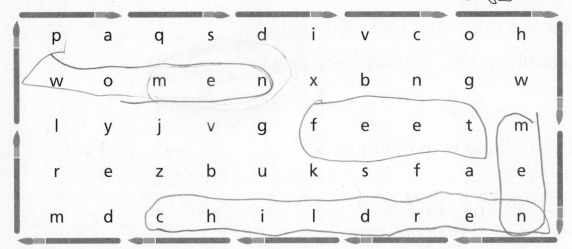

p	a	q	s	d	i	v	c	o	h
w	o	m	e	n	x	b	n	g	w
l	y	j	v	g	f	e	e	t	m
r	e	z	b	u	k	s	f	a	e
m	d	c	h	i	l	d	r	e	n

Use each circled word in a sentence.

1. The men are working at the construction site.

2. The women are praying.

3. I have big feet.

4. You have three children.

A Web of Friends

Here is a simple web of friends for **Ruby the Copycat**.

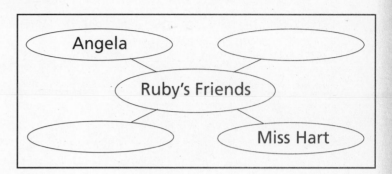

Friends may live far away or nearby.

Do you have friends who live far away? Write their names.

_____

One of Ruby's friends is her age. Another friend is a grownup.

Do you have friends of different ages? Write their names.

_____

What does friendship mean to you? Finish the sentence.

A friend is someone who _____

_____

Make **your** web of friends on another sheet of paper. Copy your sentence about friendship at the top of the page.

Check your work.

☐ I showed friends who are near and far away and of different ages.

☐ I wrote a sentence about friendship.

☐ I can explain why my friends are good friends.

MY
HANDBOOK

Contents

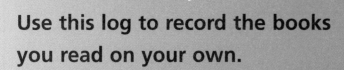

MY READING LOG

Use this log to record the books
you read on your own.

Name of Book _____

Author _____

This book is about _____

_____

_____

_____

Name of Book _____

Author _____

This book is about _____

_____

_____

_____

Name of Book _____

Author _____

This book is about _____

_____

_____

_____

Name of Book _____

Author _____

This book is about _____

_____

_____

_____

Name of Book _____

Author _____

This book is about _____

_____

_____

_____

Name of Book _____

Author _____

This book is about _____

_____

_____

_____

Name of Book _____

Author _____

This book is about _____

_____

_____

_____

Name of Book _____

Author _____

This book is about _____

_____

_____

_____

Name of Book _____

Author _____

This book is about _____

_____

_____

Name of Book _____

Author _____

This book is about _____

_____

_____

Name of Book _____

Author _____

This book is about _____

_____

_____

Trace and write the letters.

Aa Aa

Bb Bb

Cc Cc

Dd Dd

Ee Ee

Ff Ff

Gg Gg

McDougal, Littell 1993 Handwriting (continuous stroke)

Trace and write the letters.

Hh Hh

Ii Ii

Jj Jj

Kk Kk

Ll Ll

Mm Mm

McDougal, Littell 1993 Handwriting (continuous stroke)

HANDWRITING MODELS

Trace and write the letters.

Nn Nn

Oo Oo

Pp Pp

Qq Qq

Rr Rr

Ss Ss

Tt Tt

Trace and write the letters.

Uu Uu

Vv Vv

Ww Ww

Xx Xx

Yy Yy

Zz Zz

McDougal, Littell 1993 Handwriting (continuous stroke)

Trace and write the letters.

Aa Aa

Bb Bb

Cc Cc

Dd Dd

Ee Ee

Ff Ff

Gg Gg

Trace and write the letters.

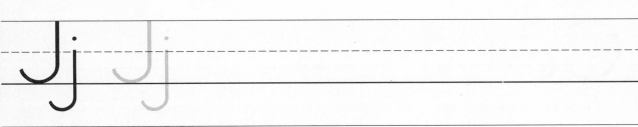

McDougal, Littell 1990 Handwriting (ball and stick)

Trace and write the letters.

Nn Nn

Oo Oo

Pp Pp

Qq Qq

Rr Rr

Ss Ss

Tt Tt

McDougal, Littell 1990 Handwriting (ball and stick)

Handwriting Models 147

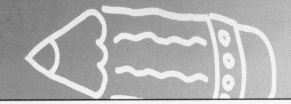

Trace and write the letters.

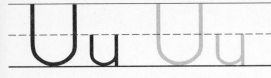

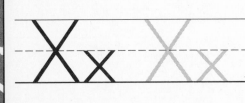

McDougal, Littell 1990 Handwriting (ball and stick)

How to Study a Word

1 **LOOK** at the word.
- What does the word mean?
- What letters are in the word?
- Name and touch each letter.

2 **SAY** the word.
- Listen for the consonant sounds.
- Listen for the vowel sounds.

3 **THINK** about the word.
- How is each sound spelled?
- Close your eyes and picture the word.
- What other words have the same spelling patterns?

4 **WRITE** the word.
- Think about the sounds and the letters.
- Form the letters correctly.

5 **CHECK** the spelling.
- Did you spell the word the same way it is spelled in your word list?
- Write the word again if you did not spell it correctly.

WORDS OFTEN MISSPELLED

A
again
already
any
are

B
been
believe
blue
both
bread
break
breakfast
brother
buy

C
come
could
country

D
do
does
doesn't
done
door

E
electric
eye

F
falling
feet
friend
from

G
give
glove
gone
great

H
half
have
head
helpful

I
I
isn't

J
judge
July

K
key

L
laugh
let's
live
lose
love
lying

M
many
money

N
neighbor
noise
no one
none
nothing

O
of
off

P
people
picnic
pretty

Q
quiet
quit

R
roar
rolling

S
said
sew
some

T
teeth
they
think
to
toe
too
two

U
until

V
voice

W
want
warm
was
wash
watch
what
who

Y
you
your

1 A short vowel sound may be spelled **a, e, i, o,** or **u**.

hat	top
pet	fun
pin	

2 Two consonant sounds said close together may be spelled **st, tr, dr, gl, ft, sl,** or **ld**.

star	**gl**ad
ju**st**	le**ft**
trip	**sl**ip
drove	o**ld**

3 The sound that begins **show** may be spelled **sh**, and the sound that ends **much** may be spelled **ch**.

she	**ch**in
wi**sh**	mu**ch**

4 The sound that begins **when** may be spelled **wh**. The sounds that begin **thin** and **that** are both spelled **th**.

what	wi**th**
there	

5 The long **a** sound may be spelled **ai, ay,** or **a**-consonant-**e**.

tr**ai**n	m**a**d**e**
pl**ay**	g**a**m**e**

6 The long **e** sound may be spelled **ee, ea,** or **e**-consonant-**e**.

t**ea**m	n**ee**d
r**ea**d	th**e**s**e**

7 The long **o** sound may be spelled **oa, ow,** or **o**-consonant-**e**.

c**oa**t	h**o**m**e**
sl**ow**	

8 The long **i** sound may be spelled **i**-consonant-**e**.

s**ize** l**i**k**e**

9 The long **u** sound may be spelled **u**-consonant-**e**.

us**e** c**u**t**e**

10 Words that end with **nd** have both the **n** and **d** sounds.

sa**nd** a**nd**

11 In words that end with **ng** or **nk**, you may not hear the **n** sound.

thi**ng** ho**nk**

12 In **contractions**, an apostrophe takes the place of a missing letter or letters.

you're we'll
it's don't

13 Add **s** to most words to mean more than one. When a word ends with **s, x, sh,** or **ch,** add **es** to name more than one.

coat**s** wi**shes**
bus**es** pea**ches**
bo**xes**

14 The final **e** in some words is dropped before adding **ed** or **ing.**

shar**ed** tak**ing**

15 The final consonant in some words is doubled before adding **ed** or **ing.**

stop**ped** hug**ging**

16 The vowel sound in **ball** may be spelled **aw** or **a** before **ll.**

saw   c**a**ll

17 The vowel sound in **boy** may be spelled **oi** or **oy**.

oil   j**oy**

18 The vowel sound in **cow** may be spelled **ow** or **ou**.

d**ow**n   m**ou**se

19 The vowel + **r** sounds may be spelled **ar, or, ore,** or **er**.

arm   st**ore**

b**or**n   ov**er**

20 The vowel sound in **moon** may be spelled **oo**.

r**oo**m   s**oo**n

21 The vowel sound in **book** may be spelled **oo**.

f**oo**t   l**oo**k

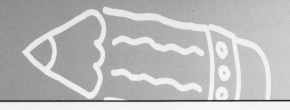

GRAMMAR GUIDE

Grammar, Capitalization, and Punctuation

SENTENCES

A **sentence** tells what someone or something did.

> We ate dinner. The boy rode the bus.

Kinds of Sentences

A **telling sentence** tells something. It begins with a capital letter. It ends with a period.

> The horse won the race. Cathy went to the store.

A **question** asks something. It begins with a capital letter. It ends with a question mark.

> Are you hungry? Do you like to play soccer?

An **exclamation** shows strong feeling. It begins with a capital letter. It ends with an exclamation point.

> I loved that book! What a fun day that was!

Naming Parts and Action Parts

Every sentence has a **naming part** and an **action part.**

The **naming part** of a sentence tells who or what.

> **Jennifer** played in the snow. **The sky** looks beautiful today.

The **action part** of a sentence tells what is happening.

The train **moves fast.**   Alex **laughs.**

NOUNS

A **noun** names a person, a place, or a thing.

The **girl** likes to run.   We saw the **pig**.

Shelley went to the **park**.

Special Nouns

Some nouns name special people, places, or things.

These **special nouns** begin with capital letters.

Nouns	Special Nouns
My **dog** loves to play.	**Fluffy** loves to play.
The **park** is her favorite place.	**Jefferson Park** is her favorite place.

Nouns for One and More Than One

A noun can name one person, place, or thing.

Tommy picked up the **cat**.   She walked by the **tree**.

A noun can also name more than one person, place, or thing.

Tommy picked up the **cats**.   She walked by the **trees**.

Add **s** to most nouns to name more than one.

    The rug**s** were wet.   The hat**s** were silly.

Add **es** to nouns that end with **s, x, ch,** and **sh**
to name more than one.

    These glass**es** are old.   The watch**es** need to be fixed.

    The fox**es** were playing.   The dish**es** are dry.

A few nouns change their spelling to name more than one.

    one child → two child**ren**   one man → two m**en**

    one foot → two f**ee**t   one woman → two wom**en**

PRONOUNS

A **pronoun** can take the place of a noun.

He, she, it, and **they** are pronouns.

Karen likes to swim.	**She** likes to swim.
Brett likes to swim too.	**He** likes to swim too.
Maria and Brett meet Karen at the pool.	**They** meet Karen at the pool.
The water is very warm.	**It** is very warm.

VERBS

A **verb** names an action.

Mary **plays** the piano beautifully.

The birds **fly** over the trees.

The baby **drinks** the juice.

I **get** my lunch.

Verbs That Tell About Now

A verb can tell about an action that is happening now.

Add **s** to a verb that tells about one.

The cat **plays** with the ball.   Tricia **smiles**.

Do not add **s** to a verb that tells about more than one.

The boys **sing** songs.

Verbs That Tell About the Past

A verb can name actions that happened before now, or in the past.

Add **ed** to a verb to show that something happened in the past.

We **walked** to the store.

Marta **called** her on the phone.

Kim **rowed** the boat to safety.

Is, Are, Was, Were

Is and **are** tell about something that is happening **now**.

Use **is** with one. Use **are** with more than one.

Mr. Roberts **is** my teacher.   They **are** at home.

Was and **were** tell about something that happened in the past.

I **was** at the party yesterday.   My friends **were** already there.

Irregular Verbs

Some special verbs change spelling to tell about the past.

Have and **Do**

William **has** fun at the fair.   He **does** like hats.

People **have** fun at the fair.   They **do** like hats.

They **had** fun at the fair.   She **did** like hats.

Take and **Make**

He **takes** some cookies.   He **makes** toys.

They **take** some cookies.   The girls **make** toys.

We **took** some cookies.   Everyone **made** toys.

Throw and **Break**

Jimmy **throws** the ball.   The man **breaks** the glass.

The players **throw** the ball.   The workers **break** the glass.

Kara **threw** the ball.   The dog **broke** the glass.

ADJECTIVES

An **adjective** is a word that tells how something looks, feels, tastes, smells, and sounds.

The **pretty** sunset made them happy. (looks)

The child was sleeping in a **soft** blanket. (feels)

The pizza was **spicy**. (tastes)

Many flowers have a **sweet** smell. (smells)

The **loud** siren scared her. (sounds)

Adjectives can also tell size, shape, color, and how many.

The **large** cloud moved slowly. (size)

The child had a **round** face. (shape)

The **blue** hat is in the box. (color)

Two workers walked into the building. (how many)

Comparing with Adjectives

Add **er** to adjectives to compare two people, places, or things.

Lupe had **shorter** hair than Kelly.

Add **est** to compare more than two people, places, or things.

Lee had the **shortest** hair in the class.

GRAMMAR GUIDE

CAPITALIZATION

Every sentence begins with a capital letter.

The weather is sunny.

The names of the days of the week begin with capital letters.

The party is on **T**uesday.

The names of months begin with capital letters.

We go camping every year in **A**ugust.

The names of holidays begin with capital letters.

I want to buy my mother a **M**other's **D**ay gift.

A title begins with a capital letter.

Put a period after **Mrs.**, **Mr.**, **Ms.**, and **Dr.**

The title **Miss** does not have a period.

Mrs. Jackson	**Ms.** Sloane	**Dr.** Lee
Mr. Fernandez	**Miss** Jones	

The first word, the last word, and each important word in a book title begin with a capital letter. Book titles are underlined.

I like the book **B**ringing the **R**ain to **K**apiti **P**lain.

PUNCTUATION

Ending Sentences

A telling sentence ends with a period.

> All of Timmy's friends will be at the party.

A question ends with a question mark.

> Will there be balloons and cake at the party?

An exclamation ends with an exclamation point.

> That cake was really good!

Contractions

Use an apostrophe in contractions to take the place of missing letters.

isn't (is not)	it's (it is)
can't (cannot)	I'm (I am)
wouldn't (would not)	they've (they have)
wasn't (was not)	they'll (they will)
we're (we are)	you're (you are)

Comma

Use a comma between the day and the year in dates.

> My sister was born August 22, 1995.

Use a comma between the name of a city and the name of a state.

> We went on a trip to Phoenix, Arizona.
>
> Her family lives in San Jose, California.

PROOFREADING CHECKLIST

Read each question. Check your paper for each kind of mistake. Correct any mistakes you find.

- ☐ Did I begin each sentence with a capital letter?
- ☐ Did I use the correct end mark?
- ☐ Did I spell each word correctly?
- ☐ Did I indent each paragraph?

PROOFREADING MARKS		
∧	Add one or more words.	want to I ∧ see the play.
—	Take out one or more words. Change the spelling.	The boat ~~did~~ moved slowly. filled The cloud ~~filed~~ the sky.
/	Make a capital letter a small letter.	The A̸nimals hid from the storm.
=	Make a small letter a capital letter.	There are thirty days in april.

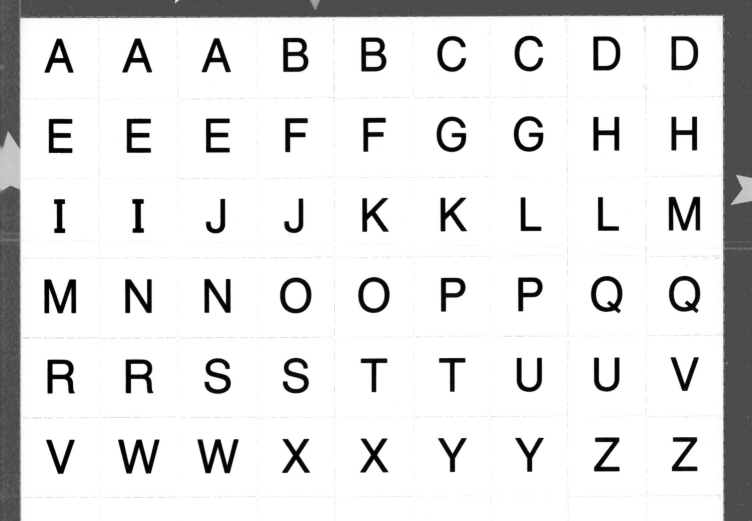

A	A	A	B	B	C	C	D	D
E	E	E	F	F	G	G	H	H
I	I	J	J	K	K	L	L	M
M	N	N	O	O	P	P	Q	Q
R	R	S	S	T	T	U	U	V
V	W	W	X	X	Y	Y	Z	Z

Letter Tray
▼

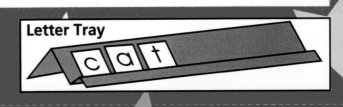

Letter Tray

fold

fold

fold

d	d	c	c	b	b	a	a	a
h	h	g	g	f	f	e	e	e
m	l	l	k	k	j	j	i	i
q	q	p	p	o	o	n	n	m
v	u	u	t	t	s	s	r	r
z	z	y	y	x	x	w	w	v

fold

fold

fold

| JULIUS | ARTHUR'S PET BUSINESS | THE CATS OF TIFFANY STREET |
High-Frequency Words	High-Frequency Words	High-Frequency Words
better	care	end
?	?	?
hour	night	family
?	?	?
pick	thank	far
?	?	?
stay	these	left
?	?	?
told	watch	quietly
?	?	?
	well	street
?	?	?
?	?	?
?	?	?
?	?	?
?	?	?

THE CATS OF TIFFANY STREET	ARTHUR'S PET BUSINESS	JULIUS
Spelling Words	Spelling Words	Spelling Words
left	dish	that
?	?	?
just	she	them
?	?	?
stay	much	when
?	?	?
old	cash	with
?	?	?
slip	chin	than
?	?	?
drove	wish	white
?	?	?
trip	such	thin
?	?	?
glad	chop	which
?	?	?
climb	brush	think
?	?	?
floor	leash	where
?	?	?

WHERE DOES THE TRAIL LEAD? High-Frequency Words	WHAT LIVES IN A SHELL? High-Frequency Words	NATURE SPY High-Frequency Words	ANIMAL TRACKS High-Frequency Words
brown	does	bird	animal
?	?	?	?
island	goes	close	another
?	?	?	?
lead	grow	eye	been
?	?	?	?
sea	most	green	car
?	?	?	?
smell	open	size	drink
?	?	?	?
		small	once
?	?	?	?
?	?	?	?
?	?	?	?
?	?	?	?
?	?	?	?

ANIMAL TRACKS	NATURE SPY	WHAT LIVES IN A SHELL?	WHERE DOES THE TRAIL LEAD?
Spelling Words	Spelling Words	Spelling Words	Spelling Words
mud	web	home	sand
?	?	?	?
is	rock	game	sink
?	?	?	?
ran	nest	made	and
?	?	?	?
has	pod	use	wind
?	?	?	?
jump	spot	close	honk
?	?	?	?
fast	leg	like	thing
?	?	?	?
cut	pet	size	thank
?	?	?	?
fish	job	these	sing
?	?	?	?
tracks	shell	inside	along
?	?	?	?
until	else	race	among
?	?	?	?

RUBY THE COPYCAT	WHAT KIND OF BABY-SITTER IS THIS?	WATCH OUT, RONALD MORGAN!	MY FIRST AMERICAN FRIEND
High-Frequency Words	High-Frequency Words	High-Frequency Words	High-Frequency Words
black	boy	best	didn't
?	?	?	?
both	heard	blue	fly
?	?	?	?
dear	miss	don't	girl
?	?	?	?
ever	through	round	last
?	?	?	?
pretty	while	still	myself
?	?	?	?
write	wish		soon
?	?	?	?
?	?	?	?
?	?	?	?
?	?	?	?
?	?	?	?

MY FIRST AMERICAN FRIEND	WATCH OUT, RONALD MORGAN!	WHAT KIND OF BABY-SITTER IS THIS?	RUBY THE COPYCAT
Spelling Words	Spelling Words	Spelling Words	Spelling Words
train	see	own	I'm
?	?	?	?
play	read	soap	don't
?	?	?	?
day	need	coat	it's
?	?	?	?
paint	please	show	didn't
?	?	?	?
way	team	bowl	that's
?	?	?	?
rain	green	slow	we'll
?	?	?	?
sail	speak	road	isn't
?	?	?	?
pay	feed	boat	you're
?	?	?	?
always	sneakers	know	who's
?	?	?	?
afraid	agree	tomorrow	wouldn't
?	?	?	?

once	well	end
bird	better	family
close	hour	far
eye	pick	left
green	stay	quietly
size	told	street
small	animal	care
does	another	night
goes	been	thank
grow	car	these
most	drink	watch

wish	soon	open
black	best	brown
both	blue	island
dear	don't	lead
ever	round	sea
pretty	still	smell
write	boy	didn't
	heard	fly
	miss	girl
	through	last
	while	myself